RECONSTRUCTING
HOPE

Intrusions, Oxymorons &
Transformations in the
Breast Cancer Marathon

Donna Sidwell DeGracia

ISBN 13: 978-1-63489-360-2

Library of Congress Catalog Number: 2020912497
Printed in the United States of America
First Printing: 2020
24 23 22 21 20   5 4 3 2 1

Cover design by Zoe Norvell
Interior design by Cindy Samargia Laun

Wise Ink Creative Publishing
807 Broadway St. NE, Suite 46
Minneapolis, MN 55413
wiseink.com

To order, visit itascabooks.com or call 1-800-901-3480.
Reseller discounts available.

"Cancer is a passport to intimacy. It is an invitation, maybe even a mandate, to enter the most vital arenas of human life, the most sensitive and the most frightening, the ones that we never want to go to—but when we do go there, we feel incredibly transformed."

—BRUCE FEILER

TABLE OF CONTENTS

ACKNOWLEDGMENTS

This book has been a work of love that would not have been possible without the help and encouragement of many.

First, I need to acknowledge those who inspired me by their courage and strength through disease and even death. They are the angels who sat on my shoulder giving me the perseverance to continue and the belief in this work.

I would like to thank all the friends and family who encouraged me to take on this project and who believed in my ability to see it through.

I would especially like to thank Cora Peine and Megan Webber for their helpful suggestions as readers and editors.

A special thanks to Tara Rick, who provided contacts for some of the interviews that made this book possible, and to Dr. Douglas Yee for his review of medical content.

Most of all, I would like to thank all the survivors, family members, and friends who shared their stories with me and helped me to understand the depth and breadth of the breast cancer experience. These are the stories that added perspective and turned my single voice into a symphony. Their stories, poetry, and insight have helped me to process my own breast cancer experience and to become a more compassionate medical provider through better understanding the humanity of disease. I will long remember the laughter and the tears we shared.

INTRODUCTION

When I was first diagnosed with breast cancer, I resented the intrusion on my busy life and wanted to move on as quickly as possible. My approach was that of a sprinter: run fast and hard and finish quickly. I worked with my doctors to develop a treatment plan that would do just that. Six weeks after my initial diagnosis I was leading a group of graduate students through Nicaragua. I thought the race was over. I was cancer free. I had won . . . or so I thought.

Over time I learned that my journey was not over when treatment ended. I had a lot of adjustments to make. I needed to learn to live with cancer.

The *survivor* label is not earned by completing treatment and being deemed cancer free. Instead, one earns that label at the time of diagnosis and carries it with them from that point on. Cancer is not a sprint. One does not finish the race and return to life as it was before. It is more like a marathon over uneven terrain, one that continues well after treatment is finished.

The beginning of the race may resemble a sprint. One starts out running as hard and fast as possible, trying to beat the disease. Over time, circumstances change and the pace slows. The patient, like the long-distance runner, finds a new rhythm. That rhythm constantly readjusts to the course. There are highs and lows, hills and valleys along the way.

Some challenges seem insurmountable, but around other corners the runner may encounter breathtaking beauty or a group of supporters waiting to cheer them on. Breast cancer survivors, like marathon runners, have highs and lows. The journey is dotted with oxymorons and unexpected contradictions that illustrate the strength and beauty of the human spirit. It reminds them that they are loved and of the simple joy of living.

Running a marathon is an amazing accomplishment, evidence of hard work and tenacity. It builds character. Traversing the breast cancer journey transforms life as well. I know my life has been forever changed, as have the lives of countless others. We have persisted, we have grown, we are transformed, and our journeys have transformed the lives of others.

Part 1

INTRUSIONS:
THE INSIDIOUS DISEASE

Collapse of My Belief System: A Nativity Scene

Cancer has made me purge every niche of my belief system.
Expectations are being discarded from the corners of my soul.
Nothing is left untouched or unexamined.
Beliefs never questioned are being cut to the bare bone.
Is there anything left that I can trust?
The contents of my mind are wrung through a wringer
Squeezing out certainties I have held dear.
The entire foundation is crumbling, brick by brick.
All that is left is doubt and fear.
The cupboard is bare and I am so hungry.
How can a lifetime of carefully selected beliefs
evaporate so quickly?

Must I erase the slate clean in order to be reborn,
To come into the world naked?
I am in the birth canal.
Painful contractions press me toward the opening.
Is this what the baby feels in the final stages of labor?
Or the caterpillar emerging from the darkness
of the cocoon?

I long to unfold my wet wings and model their
brilliant colors
To see the light and feel the energy of the sun.
I want to fly unburdened
Like a helium balloon unleashed from the weight
that held it down.
I yearn to truly know God and be filled with her love.

—GAY WALKER

Chapter 1

THE GAME HAS
CHANGED

The author and her friend Annette with siblings and author's mother.

———————————

From one day it's one way, and the next day the chessboard of your life has been completely thrown up in the air. You figure out what you're going to do and how you're going to do it with all the ignorance and fear.

—DICK HURRELBRINK

MY STORY

When I was twenty-one, I had my palm read. The ancient fortune-teller held my hand in his and traced the lines on my palm. He told me many things about myself and about my future. At the end of the reading, he said, "You will live a very long life, but your life line is broken. You will have a major interruption."

Thirty-four years later, I received the diagnosis of breast cancer, a disease that intrudes on many lives. One in eight women in the United States will develop invasive breast cancer in her lifetime, and more women die from breast cancer in the US than any other type except lung cancer.[1] Incidence and survival rates vary greatly throughout the world, but breast cancer prevalence is increasing, and it is the top cancer in women worldwide.[2] Most of us know someone who carries a breast cancer diagnosis.

I had three good friends growing up. Our friendship started when we were hardly more than toddlers; we spent hours together each day, often huddled around a reel-to-reel tape recorder listening breathlessly as Peter captured the fearsome wolf that threatened him and his animal friends. Sergei Prokofiev's musical portrayal of a small boy's fearless battle in his famous *Peter and the Wolf* drew four friends together day after day. We couldn't get enough. That early experience bound us together for life.

This is my first memory of friendship and the first marker in my own breast cancer story. Back then, so many years ago, none of us could have imagined that the bond we shared as children would become the sisterhood of cancer.

Childhood was a magical time filled with sleepovers and exploration. Gail and I were the adventurers. We climbed out on the rocks while the incoming tide sent waves crashing around

---

1   "Your Risk of Breast Cancer," breastcancer.org, https://www.breastcancer.org/risk/understand/your_risk.

2   "Breast Cancer: Prevention and Control," World Health Organization, https://www.who.int/cancer/detection/breastcancer/en/index1.html.

us and stayed until the water rose so high that we had to swim back to shore. We shared a love of art and adventure. Gail had an infectious smile that endeared her to everyone. I was shy and often resided in her shadow.

Annette was the spiritual one. She knew from childhood that she would marry a minister and remain steeped in faith. She was likely to abstain from the adventures and instead stand by nervously, waiting to ensure Gail's and my safety, perhaps saying a little prayer to protect us from our own foolishness. Everyone loved Annette for her honest and caring nature.

Ruth Ann was the big sister. She kept us in line to the best of her limited ability. More often than not, though, after she stomped her foot and tried to stare us down, we would find a way to dissolve her frown into uncontrolled giggling.

The four of us shared a bond so strong that no physical distance or time apart could break it. Despite decades of separation during adulthood, we remained close in spirit and supported one another until the end.

Unfortunately, life was interrupted too soon for us as one by one we were diagnosed with breast cancer. We weren't all as victorious as little Peter had been against the wolf. I am the only one left in this world now. The others survive only as memories.

Ruth Ann was the first. I had not seen her for years; after her diagnosis, Gail kept me up to date by phone. Her family's fear rapidly replaced hope as her condition deteriorated and conventional treatments failed. She died too quickly.

Gail was next. Her diagnosis was early enough that her treatment was a simple lumpectomy. My own breast cancer also seemed like little more than a small inconvenience. I wanted to deal with it decisively, quickly, and move on.

Annette was the last one diagnosed. She lived too far away for me to see her often during her illness, but that didn't stop me from supporting my friend. Gail and I were able to provide the support that only people who have shared the experience can provide. We kept in touch by email. Annette relied on her faith and prayed for a miracle that never came. Reading between the lines of her updates, I could tell that things weren't going well. Gail and I talked about how to help, but there was very little time. All we could do was hold her hand when we were finally together and offer unspoken support. Her death was hard. A cloud of loneliness hovered over me for a long time. I felt very alone. With Ruth Ann and Annette both gone, our childhood seemed almost erased.

Gail and I considered ourselves the lucky ones because we had been diagnosed early. We were the survivors. Imagine my surprise when, after a couple years of separation, I saw a picture of Gail on Facebook that showed the ravages of disease on her face and body. She had developed ovarian cancer, a disease that has an affinity for those with genetic forms of breast cancer.

Gail's death left me feeling empty and even more alone. The magic of our childhood was gone. There was no one left to share the memories. The game had changed forever—and it is not over. I am the lone survivor, but breast cancer is not in my past. It continues to intrude upon my life. Twelve years after my original diagnosis, it decided to play an encore.

CHANGES IN GLOBAL EPIDEMIOLOGY

Epidemiologists look at statistics and try to determine the reasons for change in the prevalence of disease. What they know about breast cancer is that it is on the rise. We know some of the reasons for the increase, but not others.

There has been an increase in the rates of cancer generally and of other chronic diseases, especially in developing countries. One reason is that people are living longer. In the past, infectious diseases killed many people; now that more people are immunized against a variety of diseases, and the HIV/AIDS pandemic and other infectious diseases are under better control, people are living longer and thus have more time to develop chronic diseases, such as cancer and heart disease. Health infrastructure in many countries is having difficulty keeping up with the change.

Clinicians in poorer countries often don't have as much experience as those in wealthier places with managing chronic diseases, and their health systems don't have the capacity for sufficient screening and treatment options. The result is that many breast cancers in developing countries have a very poor prognosis because they are diagnosed at a late stage and have few treatment options. A diagnosis of breast cancer in these countries often equates to a death sentence.

Risk factors and lifestyle also affect breast cancer rates. While we don't understand all the risk factors, obesity and alcohol have been implicated. As countries develop, individual income and access to food and other commercial products increase. Obesity rates and alcohol consumption are on the rise along with breast cancer rates.[3]

A combination of factors means that while incidence is rising, survival rates vary widely throughout the world. The World Health Organization reports survival rates of over 80 percent in North America, Sweden, and Japan and below 40 percent in low-income countries.[4]

The Susan G. Komen organization predicts that breast cancer will increase by 82 percent in Tanzania by 2025. Currently

3 "What Are the Risk Factors for Breast Cancer?", Center for Disease Control and Prevention, https://www.cdc.gov/cancer/breast/basic_info/risk_factors.html.

4 "Breast Cancer: Prevention and Control," World Health Organization, https://www.who.int/cancer/detection/breastcancer/en/index1.html.

mammograms and chemotherapy are not available at local or even district health centers, and radiation therapy is only available at the national level.[5] This makes treating cancer difficult.

I talked to Halima, a woman from Tanzania, about her experience with breast cancer. Halima was born in the Kilimanjaro Region in northern Tanzania. After receiving her education, she rose to the position of provincial governor.

During her time as governor, she developed symptoms that, in retrospect, were consistent with advanced cancer. Halima was lucky—she had access to the best health care available in her country. An ultrasound showed nothing, but finally a biopsy confirmed the presence of a tumor.

After the biopsy, she was referred from the public hospital to a private hospital where a mammogram was available, and her breast cancer diagnosis was confirmed. When Halima asked about treatment, the doctor gave her an honest answer:

> "Mama, we don't know the extent of the spread of your cancer. What we do here, we don't have the screening facilities. We just do mastectomy, then we just leave it. You are educated. I must tell you the truth: sometimes we just do the mastectomy to satisfy the woman, but there's nothing more we can do about it. We don't have the cobalt, the radiation, and the hormone therapy that treats the whole body system."

Halima's situation is not isolated to Tanzania but rather represents a widespread lack of access to care in developing countries. She was able to receive care in the United States, but a woman without Halima's status, financial means, and connections has very few options for care.

---

5   Susan G. Komen, *Tanzania Breast Health Care Assessment 2017: An Assessment of Breast Cancer Early Detection, Diagnosis and Treatment in Tanzania*, 2017, https://ww5.komen.org/Tanzania/HSAReport/Tanzania2017.

MORTALITY VARIATIONS:
WHY DO SOME PEOPLE DIE AND SOME PEOPLE LIVE?

Breast cancer is a strange disease. It takes many different forms. It can occur in different parts of the breast and can respond to different stimuli. It is also very good at hiding and moving to other parts of the body. Some breast cancers have relatives that can attack other organs. Survival depends on a number of factors.

One of the most important factors has to do with detection. In general, the earlier the cancer is detected, the easier it is to treat and the better the prognosis. Another factor is the specifics of the cancer itself. Some cancers are harder to treat than others or do not respond as well to traditional treatments. Some are more likely to return.

Another important factor is access to treatment. It doesn't help to find a cancer early if there is limited or no treatment available. If a patient doesn't have insurance or another way to pay for treatment, they may have to make difficult decisions about how to use their limited finances. In some places, treatment options are very limited. This is particularly true in developing countries, but even in the United States, many advanced therapies simply don't exist for someone who does not have the ability to travel to a major medical center and receive treatment there.

Host characteristics are another important determining factor. Many people with breast cancer are older or have other health conditions or comorbidities that interfere with the ability of their bodies to fight the cancer and withstand the effects of treatment. They may be on medications that interfere with some treatment options, making it important to weigh the risks and benefits of options. This can result in choosing an option other than the one that might otherwise be someone's first choice. And younger women and others receiving hormone therapy have higher levels of certain hormones that can feed some breast cancers, which means their cancer may be more aggressive and faster growing.

No two patients and no two cancers are the same. A patient and their care team need to do their best to evaluate both the cancer and the patient and choose the plan that best fits their goals and their life and has the best chance of eradicating, or at least controlling, the cancer.

TYPES OF DISEASE

In order to understand the physical impact of breast cancer and the different approaches to treatment, it is necessary to understand the structure and function of breasts. Female breasts are complex structures made up of fat, connective tissues (such as muscles), lobes, lobules, ducts, and lymph nodes. Lobules are collections of small balloon-like structures that branch out from the nipple. This is where the breast makes milk. A series of tubes, called ducts, links the lobules together. These ducts carry breast milk from the lobules toward the areola (the darker part around the nipple), where ducts join together into larger ducts that end at the nipple. This is similar to how streams and other tributaries join together to make a river. Fat fills the spaces around the lobules. The milk-producing structures of the breast are pretty much the same in all people who have them, but the amount of fat varies and increases with age as the milk-producing structures atrophy. While not all breast cancer patients have the female breast structure, all breasts respond to hormones and have the potential to develop cancer.

Lymph nodes that surround breast tissue drain the breast and help prevent infection. These lymph nodes are very important in the evaluation of breast cancer. Tracking their involvement helps locate breast cancer and map its spread. The lymph system can transport cancer cells from the original lump to other organs, such as the brain or the bones.

Types of breast cancer correlate with the anatomical location of the cancer. About one in five new breast cancers is **ductal carcinoma in situ (DCIS)**, which means abnormal cells in the lining of the milk duct. This cancer is noninvasive—it has not spread outside of the ducts. Because it is well contained within the ducts, it is easily treated. If it is not treated, however, it can spread outside the ducts. Newer screening tools have improved diagnosis of DCIS and increased survival rates for patients whose cancer is detected in this early stage.

When the abnormal cells in the ducts spread outside of the ducts, it becomes **invasive ductal carcinoma (IDC)**. This cancer can spread to other parts of the body. It is the most common breast cancer in those assigned male at birth and a large percentage of overall breast cancer diagnoses. Invasive ductal carcinoma occurs when DCIS is not detected and treated before it can spread.

Lobular carcinoma in situ (LCIS) is the term for cells that look like cancer and have been found in the lobules but have not invaded through the walls of the lobules. This cancer lives in the lobules instead of the ducts.

Invasive lobular breast cancer occurs when the cancer is located in the lobules. This is the same as LCIS but at a slightly more advanced stage. These cancers do not always cause lumps in the breast. Patients with cancer in the lobules have a significantly increased risk of developing invasive cancer in either breast. Sometimes this type of cancer causes a thickened area in the breast or, if the tumor is large, dimpling in the breast. These tumors can be difficult to see on mammograms and may need biopsy and analysis of the material collected for diagnosis. Lymph node evaluation is usually necessary to assess whether the cancer has spread to other parts of the body. I have lobular breast cancer, and the fact that this type of cancer has a significant chance of reoccurring in either breast was a major factor in my treatment decision. These cancers are usually **estrogen receptor–positive**, which is also important for choosing treatment. Tumors that have estrogen receptors often respond to medications that block these receptors and may not need harsher chemotherapy.

Paget's disease of the nipple is a relatively rare form of breast cancer that starts in the ducts and spreads to the skin of the nipple and areola. This form of cancer is usually associated with ductal disease, such as DCIS or ductal carcinoma. Early symptoms may include burning or itching. If it remains untreated, characteristic skin changes will occur starting at the nipple. The breast may develop sores that will not heal. Paget's disease can be mistaken for a skin disorder, which can delay diagnosis and treatment.

Inflammatory breast cancers are a rare group of cancers. In inflammatory breast cancer, cancer cells infiltrate the skin and lymph vessels, the channels for drainage of breast tissue to lymph nodes. Inflammatory breast cancers often do not produce a lump or a distinct tumor. Symptoms can be subtle and nonspecific, such as persistent itching, irritation to a small area of the breast, or nipple changes such as flattening, dimpling, or inversion (when the nipple turns inward). Sometimes the breast will become red, swollen, and warm—a presentation that may look very much like mastitis, an infection or inflammation of the breast commonly seen in those who are breastfeeding. One very distinctive change related to inflammatory breast cancer is what medical providers call "orange-peel pitting." When this occurs, the skin of the breast resembles the finely pitted skin of an orange.

Angiosarcoma is another rare type of cancer that can occur in any part of the body and sometimes occurs in the breast. It can be the result of previous radiation treatment for breast cancer, particularly in older women. These cancers tend to grow and spread quickly.

Metastatic breast cancer is a term used to describe cancer that has spread beyond the breast and axilla. The most common sites of metastasis are the bone, brain, liver, and lungs. Symptoms of metastatic breast cancer can be nonspecific, such as fatigue, weight loss, or loss of appetite. Symptoms may also be specific to the site of the metastasis. Metastatic breast cancer is the most advanced form of cancer and the hardest to treat. Treatment focuses on controlling the cancer and giving the patient more time rather than curing the cancer.

Health-care providers use staging of cancers to help guide treatment and predict prognosis. They base staging on three factors: the tumor, the lymph nodes, and the spread (metastasis). Tumor staging is based on the size of the tumor. The number and location of lymph nodes with cancer cells determine lymph node staging. Survival correlates closely with the stage of the cancer at the time of diagnosis as well as specific cancer characteristics. Staging can help with decisions related to treatment.

Breast Cancer Staging[6]

0	Abnormal cells are present but have not spread to nearby tissue.
1	Cancer has spread to other tissue in a small area.
2	There is a localized small tumor and some lymph nodes are involved, or there is a slightly larger tumor with no lymph nodes involved.
3	The tumor may be larger with more lymph nodes involved over a wider region; or there is no tumor, but cancer may have spread to the skin or chest wall.
4	The cancer has spread beyond the breast to other parts of the body. This is known as metastatic cancer.

HOW BREAST CANCER GROWS AND SPREADS

Receptors on the cancer cells can be helpful in determining treatment decisions. Many newer therapies target specific receptors in an attempt to both reduce adverse effects related to treatment and prolong life.

I have lobular cancer that is estrogen receptor–positive (HR+). HR+ means that the cancer cells have receptors on them that make them grow when certain hormones are present. Knowing that my cancer is HR+ tells my oncologist that it could respond to hormone-blocking treatment. Hormone receptor blockers can decrease the incidence of recurrence in patients with HR+ cancer types even after removal of the original cancer.

Dr. George Beatson first identified the link between hormones and breast cancer in 1896 after treating a woman with breast cancer who had a tumor that he could not completely remove

---

6 "Stages of Breast Cancer," Memorial Sloan Kettering Cancer Center, https://www.mskcc.org/cancer-care/types/breast/diagnosis/stages-breast.

surgically. He remembered watching shepherds remove the ovaries of sheep to control lactation when he had worked on a farm in Scotland years before, and that memory prompted him to remove the ovaries of his patient in the hope that it would improve her chances of survival. The patient recovered and lived for many years. This was the beginning of the idea that hormones can drive breast cancer.

The role of hormones and hormone receptors in breast cancer led to research on treatment options beginning around 1960. This revolutionized assessment and treatment of breast cancer. Now, some 130 years after Dr. Beatson's experiment, we recognize that cancer cells have memory. They remember that they responded to hormones when they were normal cells, and they want to continue to do the same.

Other breast cancers have a protein receptor called human epidermal growth factor receptor 2 (HER2). The protein, in normal breast health, helps breast cells grow and repair themselves. Sometimes, however, the body produces too many of these protein receptors, causing abnormal cell growth and division in the breast. Specific antibody-based targeted therapies are available for HER2+ breast cancers.

Triple-negative breast cancers are cancers that do not have certain hormone receptors. These cancers do not have specific targeted therapies, but many traditional therapies work on them.[7]

Breast cancer is an insidious disease. There are no symptoms until the disease is advanced, so it can hide and spread without detection. The lethal aspect of the disease is the ability of the cells to leave the breast, go elsewhere, and grow in other organs. This happens in one of three ways.

The earliest spread is often direct expansion from one area in

---

7   Much of this information came from a lecture given by Dr. Douglas Yee, Department of Oncology at the University of Minnesota. Dr. Yee is a practicing oncologist specializing in breast cancer and breast cancer research.

the breast to adjacent tissues. Cancer in situ may be a precursor or a marker of increased risk for either ductal carcinoma or lobular carcinoma, depending on where it starts. It can then spread through the duct or the lobe into the supporting structures of the breast, such as the muscles. Early breast cancer treatment was only surgical; radical mastectomy was the initial treatment of choice. The thought was that removal of the breast, the pectoralis muscle under the breast, and the lymph nodes in the armpit would prevent recurrence and cure breast cancer. Later research found that there was no difference in survival between those who underwent mastectomy and those who underwent lumpectomy.

The second way that breast cancer spreads is through the lymphatic system, a series of channels through the body that are part of the immune system. Lymph channels drain into lymph nodes that connect them. As breast cancer advances, it enters the closest lymph channels and spreads to the lymph nodes that drain that part of the breast. Those lymph nodes connect to other lymph channels that go to other body organs. Once the cancer has spread to the lymph nodes or into the blood, it can easily travel to and grow in another organ or organs.

Surgeons typically remove at least some lymph nodes during breast cancer surgery to check for lymphatic spread. They look for sentinel lymph nodes, or lymph nodes that drain the tumor location. Lymph node mapping involves injecting a dye into the tumor during surgery. The lymphatic system will take the dye to the sentinel node or nodes that drain that part of the breast. The surgeon removes those nodes and sends them to pathology. If the nodes removed do not contain cancer cells, the cancer has not spread to other organs, and the prognosis is better.

Even tumors that are removed can recur and spread later. When a cancer develops years later in someone who was previously treated for cancer, it is not a new cancer. It is the same cancer that has spread through a process called micrometastasis. This is the process of cancer cell replication in which the daughter cells remember the mother cells. They are too small to detect at the time of the first diagnosis, but later on, they develop the characteristics of their mother and become cancerous. This is similar to the behavior of humans who find themselves sounding or acting like their parent even in ways they had consciously decided not to. The best way to prevent spread, especially micrometastasis, is to combine surgery and another form of treatment called adjuvant therapy. The type of adjuvant therapy can now be targeted to the type of cancer and its receptors and antibodies.

Chapter 2

FINDING WHAT LIES
DEEP
WITHIN

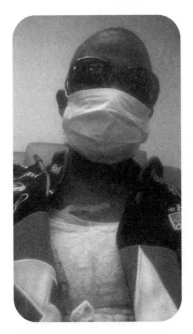

Deshanna during treatment[8]

From "**Cancer**"

You touch the bodies of the living
And mark them for dead
A plague of their own flesh
Rampant, raging, you spread.
Cruel monster, slithering
Through vessels, unknown
Multiplying, dividing
You plunder, you grow

—AMINA BHATTI

---

8 Poetry used at the beginning of each chapter is included in its entirety in
Appendix A.

SCREENING

It is easier to tame the monster before it grows and spreads its poison. Screening involves testing to find the cancer before it has caused widespread destruction. The ultimate purpose of screening is to reduce the death rate within a population. Breast cancer is a lethal disease; screening helps people survive longer. Finding a tumor when it is small and before it spreads increases survival.

Despite what we know about risk factors, there is very little we can do to eliminate breast cancer. The best we can do is to manage preventable risk factors, try to diagnose cancer in the early stages when it is most treatable, and maximize quality of life for those suffering from the disease.

Prevention is divided into three categories: primary (minimizing risk), secondary (screening), and tertiary (focusing on quality of life after diagnosis). Primary prevention aims at doing whatever is possible to minimize or eliminate risk factors for a specific disease. It targets things that the individual can change. Some risk factors, such as age and genetics, are nonmodifiable— you can't do anything about them. Others risk factors are under your control. Primary prevention of breast cancer through lifestyle modifications includes weight control, healthy eating, stress management, smoking cessation, and decreasing alcohol intake. Breastfeeding may also help prevent breast cancer.

Primary prevention also involves surgery or other treatment for some individuals. People who have a family history of genetic breast cancer and/or test positive for a mutation on the BRCA1 or BRCA2 gene may opt for prophylactic mastectomy. A prophylactic, or preventive, mastectomy is the removal of the breasts before cancer develops. This reduces the risk of developing cancer later on.

Several famous people have publicized their own choices regarding this procedure, further increasing its popularity. This is not a new practice. I know several female physicians who had prophylactic mastectomies decades ago because of positive family history. Prophylactic mastectomy is a form of primary prevention. The best protection is screening to detect cancer when it is in its earliest treatable stages, before development of signs or symptoms. Screening falls under the category of secondary prevention. The aim of secondary prevention is to detect the disease before it causes symptoms and to prevent it from progressing.

Screening modalities for breast cancer fall into the categories of exams and imaging. There have been changes in breast cancer screening recommendations since 2009 based on research around best practices. In order to understand the recommendations, it is important to understand the goals of screening and disease prevention.

A good screening test needs to meet certain requirements. First, it should screen for a condition that is relatively common, causes significant morbidity and mortality (disease and death), and is treatable. There is no point in screening people if they are not at risk for the disease, if the disease will not intrude on their lives, or if there is no treatment available.

The test should also have high sensitivity. This means it will detect the condition in most people who have it. The test needs to be specific to the target condition; if a test produces false positives (results caused by conditions other than the target condition), it can result in significant emotional stress for the patient. A screening test that has a high false-positive rate requires additional tests to determine whether the patient actually has the target condition.

Finally, a screening test needs to be acceptable. It has to produce more good than harm, it has to be reasonably affordable, and it has to be something people are willing to do.

Screening recommendations change as technology advances and research demonstrates the effectiveness of various techniques.

For breast cancer, there are multiple options with varying risks and costs, ranging from the very simple self-performed and clinical breast exams to mammograms and more advanced and expensive techniques that can be helpful but may carry additional risks. As new and better technologies are developed and studied, experts review and revise screening guidelines.

Clinicians used to teach patients to do breast self-exams, believing that if someone found a lump themselves it would speed up diagnosis and possibly save their life. The idea is to perform a self-exam at home on a monthly basis, at the end of the menstrual cycle if applicable, to detect any new or abnormal changes. When a person has a good general awareness of their own breasts and is familiar with what is normal, they may be able to recognize when something is new or abnormal.

Although few people routinely do good breast exams at home, some do detect breast cancer by self-exam.

We know that early detection is important, but today there is a lot of controversy around self-exams. The US Preventive Services Task Force recommends against physicians teaching patients how to perform a breast exam. However, the American College of Obstetricians and Gynecologists recommends performing self-breast exams because the practice can still potentially identify a palpable breast cancer, though it has not statistically been shown to save lives. This discrepancy can be confusing for patients and providers alike.

In my own practice, I have had patients come in for evaluation of a lump they found at home. Some of them have turned out to be benign, but others have been cancerous.

One patient who found a lump in her breast said that she felt a little foolish coming in because between the time she made the appointment and the time she saw me, the lump had actually decreased in size. I did a breast exam and was able to detect a very small lump. We scheduled a diagnostic mammogram. The next day she had a biopsy, which diagnosed breast cancer. She went to surgery while her cancer was still in a very early and treatable stage. For this patient, the breast self-examination was a valuable tool.

So why do the US Preventive Services Task Force and other groups discourage it now? Let's test it against the criteria for a good screening test. Breast cancer is a commonly occurring condition—I don't think there is any argument about that. It is best treated in early stages, before symptoms occur. So far, so good. Next, let's look at sensitivity. Here is where the breast self-exam starts to run into problems: sensitivity of the exam is variable. Remember, sensitive tests will pick up most abnormal findings.

Not all breasts are the same. Some are very dense, some are very large, and breast tissue extends beyond what many people think of as breasts. It is easy to miss a lump. The technique of the examiner and the characteristics of the breasts are important factors in determining the sensitivity of the exam. If the person performing the exam does not do it correctly or the breast tissue is dense or irregular, it is easy to miss significant lumps. In other words, physical variability and poor technique decrease the sensitivity of self-exams.[9]

Next, let's look at specificity, the measure of whether or not the test can correctly distinguish the targeted condition from others. Many breast lumps are not cancer, but clinicians are obligated to evaluate every lump. If a patient comes in to see a medical provider complaining of a breast lump, they are likely to have additional testing done to determine whether the lump is cancerous. This means a lot more mammograms, ultrasounds, MRIs, biopsies, and so on. Besides being costly and emotionally taxing, some of these additional tests can expose the patient to radiation or cause

---

9   See Appendix C for self-breast exam technique (no longer recommended).

scarring that may look suspicious on future mammograms and start a cycle of recurrent extraneous diagnostic tests, exposing the patient to even more potential harm and worry.

In terms of overall sensitivity, specificity, and potential harm, the breast self-examination does not measure up. However, for a given individual, it may be a good choice. The exam itself has little potential for harm. It is acceptable to patients and provides an opportunity to be proactive. Still, it is important to realize the limitations of the test and to realize that it does not replace the clinical breast exam or other recommended screening tests, such as mammograms. It is also important to be aware that a positive finding will necessitate a visit to a medical provider and likely further testing.

Many people visit a clinic on an annual basis for a complete physical. During this exam, they may have a clinical breast exam. Like the self-exam, the clinical breast exam is somewhat controversial. The US Preventive Services Task Force does not have a recommendation on clinical breast exams for patients ages forty and over, as its experts do not feel there is enough evidence to support or discourage the practice. Some clinicians may no longer be doing routine clinical breast exams and may be relying on mammograms alone for breast cancer screening. Clinical breast exams, like self-exams, vary considerably depending on the technique and expertise of the examiner as well as the individual anatomy of the patient. Some clinicians do a more thorough exam than others. A poor clinical breast exam lowers the sensitivity of the test.

For breast cancer, the most used screening tool to date has been the mammogram. When the US Preventive Services Task Force released updated screening recommendations in 2009 and revised them in 2016, it not only stopped recommending self-exams but also caused a great deal of uproar by changing the recommendations for routine mammography.[10] Before 2009, the recommendation had been that individuals without known risk factors get mammograms yearly after the age of forty. Now, the task force recommends screening for patients between the ages of fifty and seventy-four every other year. The group did not find any additional evidence supporting routine mammograms for patients over the age of seventy-five. It also did not find a benefit to routine screening with other methods of breast cancer detection.

There is still controversy surrounding routine screening of patients between the ages of forty and fifty. Even the US Preventive Services Task Force recognizes this as a gray area and allows for individual decisions between the patient and provider.

It is important to keep in mind that these recommendations represent evidence in a large population and may not be appropriate for a given individual. They are intended for people with average risk factors for developing breast cancer. It is necessary to look at family history, breast density, and other individual risk factors before deciding on a screening plan.

The American College of Obstetricians and Gynecologists and other groups are revising screening recommendations toward shared decision-making between provider and patient. Shared decision-making typically consists of providers helping patients to make informed decisions by providing them with information on the pros and cons of all options, including potential adverse effects of each. This should take into account not only medical decision-making but also consideration of unique factors within the patient's life that may make certain options more attractive or more difficult, keeping in mind that breast cancer intrudes on all aspects of life.

---

10 There are several different sets of recommendations for screening.
Links to guidelines are included in Appendix E: Websites of Interest.

Those diagnosed with breast cancer often blame themselves for not discovering their cancer on self-exam or for not getting a mammogram at the right time. They often simply do not know what they should be doing. After my initial diagnosis, I did a series of talks for Sage, Minnesota's cancer screening program, that aimed to empower people by providing education about breast cancer risks and screening. It is important for everyone to get the screening and care they need and to understand the importance of a healthy lifestyle.[11] It is also important to realize that we do not always know what causes cancer and that self-blame and speculation do more harm than good. Our best defense is good self-care and screening. Cancers caught early are usually much easier to treat.

The third category of screening is called tertiary prevention even though it does not actually prevent cancer. Its aim is to slow the progression of the disease when there is no cure and to preserve quality of life as much as possible. Tertiary prevention starts when the disease is more advanced and no longer preventable or easily treated. Treatment providers work to keep it as controlled as possible and to maximize comfort and function for the patient.

Treatment of metastatic cancer falls into the category of tertiary prevention. Once cancer has spread to organs such as the lungs or liver, or to the bones, it is difficult to cure. The goal of treatment often changes from cure to containment and preservation of quality of life.

Lisa had stage 4 breast cancer at the time of diagnosis. She explained how her treatment differed from that of those diagnosed at an earlier stage:

---

11 The Sage Screening Program is part of the Minnesota Department of Health. It provides breast and cervical screening as part of the National Breast and Cervical Cancer Early Detection Program (NBCCEDP). https://www.health.state.mn.us/diseases/cancer/sage/about/index.html

Stage 4 is very different from the early stages; in early-stage cancer, they have a much better-defined treatment protocol. It's time limited or event limited. There's an end. Whatever it is, if you're going to get surgery of some sort, chemo of some sort, radiation of some sort—they're all pretty clear, pretty straightforward. You know what the process is going to be, how long it is going to take, and, in the absence of complications and reconstruction-type issues, you're done in about eighteen months. With a stage 4 diagnosis or in somebody where the cancer has spread, that isn't the way it works. There are no real standards of treatment. There is no end, which I think is the hardest part. It just keeps going and going, and it's no longer planned.

Some patients diagnosed with stage 4 cancer do quite well. Their providers are sometimes able to keep their cancer in remission for an extended period of time, allowing patients to enjoy a meaningful quality of life.

It is important for providers to help patients with incurable cancer find hope in their situation. Hope has to be reality based and related to providing a good life for whatever time is left—and a good death when that time comes.

Providing hope at the end of life is an art form that can be challenging for providers. Breast cancer specialists are learning that it is a team effort that employs many modalities of care and extends far beyond simple diagnosis and treatment. Tertiary prevention in breast cancer care is a relatively new area of medicine that is attracting more and more attention as experts recognize the importance of shared decision-making. Social determinants of health, or a combination of life factors, affect health outcomes. Holistic treatment plans that address multiple needs can provide improved outcomes and better patient satisfaction.

THE STORY OF THE MAMMOGRAM

After the discovery of x-rays in 1895, Albert Salomon, a German surgeon, started using x-rays to examine breast cancer specimens removed during mastectomy. He began to notice common characteristics of the cancers he imaged. He published his findings in 1913.

Raul Leborgne, a radiologist in Uruguay, went a step further in 1949 by introducing the compression technique of breast imaging, the grandfather of present mammogram techniques. In the late 1950s, improved imaging techniques refined by a doctor in Texas replaced plain x-rays, and the mammogram was born.

Dr. Philip Strax studied the effectiveness of the mammogram in detection of breast cancer and effects on mortality between 1963 and 1966 and found that it could decrease mortality by 50 percent. By 1969, dedicated mammography units were available around the world.

Despite the ability of the mammogram to detect breast cancer, however, it was not widely used until well into the next decade. Early mammograms were a big breakthrough, but they were not always terribly accurate. It wasn't until 1976 that the American Cancer Society recommended routine mammogram screening. By 2009, breast cancer–related deaths had decreased by 30 percent since their peak in 1981. This decrease is largely attributable to routine mammogram and other screening as well as various adjuvant treatments now available.

In 2011, the 3D mammogram further revolutionized screening by providing increased detection ability and decreasing false positive readings. There is ongoing work on other imaging modalities, including molecular breast imaging for particularly dense breasts and breast-specific gamma imaging for high-risk patients with hard-to-detect tumors, that seem to hold promise for the future.[12]

---

12 "The History of Mammography," RamSoft, https://www.ramsoft.com/history-of-mammography.

ADDITIONAL TESTING

Breast cancer in younger patients is a particular challenge. Young breasts are typically denser and harder to examine either with a clinical exam or with mammography. It is easy to miss a small cancer in a younger person using only traditional screening tools that may be effective for older people. A young patient with risk factors for breast cancer or with lumps found on physical examination should work closely with their clinician to determine the best plan for diagnosis and treatment.

Research in breast cancer screening and evaluation is ongoing. Newer techniques may have higher sensitivity and/or specificity but are often quite expensive and require extensive evaluation to determine their applicability as screening tools. Over the next few years, we are likely to see updates in screening recommendations.

Christian, the mammogram services manager of the Jane Brattain Breast Center in Saint Louis Park, Minnesota, talked to me about how breast cancer screening has changed and what that means in terms of ability to detect breast cancer, additional screening recommendations and costs, and patient anxiety related to false positive findings and unclear guidelines.

With the advancements in technology, there are many more options than the simple mammogram. This makes screening potentially more accurate but also more confusing. Mammogram reports are now required to include an evaluation of breast tissue density. It is more difficult to detect an abnormality in a dense breast, which means there is more possibility of missing a lump with a routine mammogram. The question then becomes whether or not to employ additional or alternative screening measures for patients with dense breasts. There are no clear guidelines here.

As Christian explained:

There's 3D mammography, which is better, but it's still mammography. There's ultrasound, but the problem with ultrasound is that it does create a lot of false positives, and that's why it's not the preferred screening—because it requires an additional screening. There's contrast-enhanced mammography, where, basically, contrast is put in so it highlights those different areas. That's an option. There's a whole breast ultrasound that's an automated system. The best one that will find everything is the MRI. But MRIs cost two thousand dollars.

There's no mandated coverage for insurance. Out of the seventeen or eighteen states that have this law [requiring breast density rating], only two of them require insurance to cover further testing if you're considered dense, as a preventative measure.

So now we have the patient make that call. They're told that the mammogram might not be the best thing, but now she's going to be paying out of pocket for the rest.

An additional issue has to do with changing density. Over a person's lifetime, their breasts will change depending on hormonal influences. This means that their screening needs will also change.

Hopefully there will be additional guidelines for providers in the near future that make it much easier for patients to make informed decisions about their options, but for the present, screening involves a lot of personal decision-making with many options and just as many unknowns.

There are always new screening modalities in the pipelines. Mayo Clinic researchers are working on a simple blood test to detect cancer. The current screening does not differentiate between types of cancer, so if that screening is positive and there are no other clues as to the location of the cancer, the patient and provider need to search the whole body to find it. That involves a lot more tests, expense, and potential adverse effects.

This is an area for further research, but it is promising. If a blood test can replace the mammogram for screening, it could eliminate the factor of breast density, though it would not take away the need for additional testing of a positive result to determine the exact location and possibly the cancer type, hormone susceptibility, and other factors.

Initial screening decisions are difficult enough, but what if there is a lump? This is another challenging dilemma. The first step is clinical evaluation. The patient and their provider must determine the characteristics of the lump and the best way to proceed. At this point, a mammogram will not reveal whether or not the lump is cancerous; it can give an idea about the probability that the lump is a cancer, but it is not diagnostic. The mammogram explores the rest of the breast to look for other possible abnormalities.

Even a negative mammogram requires further investigation. Some lumps, especially if they are causing discomfort and are round and smooth and easy to find, might be aspirated in the clinic. This involves inserting a small needle into the lump and trying to draw out fluid. If there is fluid, and this technique makes the lump go away, it was probably a cyst. If the lump is completely gone, however, it is important to follow up and make sure it doesn't come back.

There are many factors to consider when deciding how to proceed with more evaluation. The first consideration is the patient themselves. Age and other risk factors need assessment—a lump in a postmenopausal patient is much more likely to be cancerous than a lump in someone younger. Other considerations are based on the characteristics of the lump. Is it easy to isolate? Is it soft or firm? Is it round or irregular? Is it movable? All of these factors help the clinician determine the best way to proceed and may help determine which evaluation modality will give the most conclusive results. Some characteristics may be more suspicious for cancer than others, but none completely rule out the possibility of cancer.

The makeup and experience of the medical team is also important. I had a fine-needle biopsy done under ultrasound to diagnose my initial cancer, which helped locate the lumps that were too small to find on exam. The ultrasound also showed the shape and density of the lumps. The first lump was round and appeared to be less dense in the middle (fluid filled). When the needle was inserted, the lump disappeared, confirming that it was a cyst. The second lump looked different. It was irregular and did not resolve when poked. The needle was able to get enough from that lump for a pathologist to determine that I had cancer.

Fine-needle biopsy is less invasive than a core biopsy, the other kind of breast biopsy, but it has limitations. First, it doesn't get as much tissue or fluid to examine. Second, it takes a well-trained technician to do the biopsy correctly, and some hospitals don't do fine-needle biopsies because they don't have the expertise. In other cases, they may not yield enough information.

A core-needle biopsy is similar to a fine-needle, or aspiration, biopsy but uses a larger, hollow needle that can extract more tissue from a lump to send to pathology for identification. The core biopsy involves a small incision and causes more bruising and swelling than a fine-needle biopsy. The patient may need ice packs or analgesics to control symptoms afterwards.

Imaging type is another consideration. A mammogram may not be enough for a definitive diagnosis. An ultrasound can help differentiate between a solid mass and a cystic or fluid-filled mass, but a biopsy is usually required for firm diagnosis. Newer imaging techniques may also be helpful but are usually more expensive than a mammogram and will still require a biopsy for more information.

The bottom line is that there are many factors to consider. A balance between sensitivity of test results, potential for physical harm or other adverse effects, and other factors related to the patient's individual circumstances is essential.

There is no "one size fits all" approach to breast cancer screening or evaluation of lumps in the breast. The patient needs to find a medical provider or team they can trust. They need someone who can answer their questions and guide them through the evaluation process. They may also need someone to help them ask the questions and remember the answers, as a cancer diagnosis can be a very emotional time.

Chapter 3

A PLAGUE OF THEIR OWN FLESH

Annie is a psychic and a breast cancer survivor.

—————————

From "**The Fact Is**"

The fact is we don't know
yet
No fractionated equation
with precisely weighted factors
tells us how the DNA
unravels
spinning cells out of order
chaotically trampling
their neighbors

What part Red Dye #3, sugar highs, omega-6 fats?
What part spiritual commitment or disconnection?
Alignment of stars?

—MORRY EDWARDS

GENETICS, FAMILY CLUSTERS, AND RISK FACTORS

Mystery, fear, and guilt all surround breast cancer. Everyone has heard of hereditary risks, but other factors can increase breast cancer risks. Cancer survivors sometimes feel guilty, thinking there was something they could have done or something they could have avoided that would have prevented the cancer. Family members often know little about hereditary patterns and assume that having a relative with breast cancer automatically puts them at high risk for developing the disease.

On a cruise to Alaska, a woman greeted us at breakfast each morning with a bottle of hand sanitizer that she sprayed on our hands as we entered the dining room. She smiled a cheery smile and said, "Washy, washy, happy, happy," sometimes followed by a happy little song. What we didn't know was that our seemingly happy server lived with constant fear. Behind the cheery façade was a story that was not nearly as happy as her morning smile would lead one to believe. She was working her second contract with the cruise line and was very much looking forward to her vacation in about seven months, when she would return to her home in the Philippines to visit her family. She was hoping to save enough money to take her mother's ashes from Manila to the family's ancestral home in the countryside.

The last time she had been home, her mother had been battling breast cancer, hoping to live long enough to see her only daughter one last time. Our server was able to visit her for that last precious bit of time to say goodbye but returned to the ship just before her mother died.

The daughter worked long hours to pay off her mother's medical bills. She was also paying college tuition for her own child and helping support her brother's family. Each morning she smiled her cheery "washy, washy" smile for the cruise-line customers, and each night she cried herself to sleep in her bunk, missing her family and mourning her mother.

In the Philippines, as in many countries, the national health services cover only the very basics. There is additional care available only for those able to pay prices that are more than the average family can afford.

Aside from worrying about the bills, this woman worried about her own future. She worked hard to support all those who depended on her back home, but there was a dark cloud hanging over her. She worried that she would develop breast cancer because of her mother's history and worried that she would not be there to take care of her loved ones. Her mother had died at the age of seventy-four, four years after diagnosis.

Many people worry that breast cancer in their family is a genetic form of breast cancer. Although having a first-degree relative with breast cancer increases the statistical risk of developing breast cancer, it is not necessarily a marker for a genetic link. Only 5 to 10 percent of breast cancers are hereditary—a small percentage of the whole. These genetically linked breast cancers often present at an earlier age.

Patients do not always know about genetics. Anita did not know a lot about breast cancer or genetics when she received her breast cancer diagnosis in 1983. She learned a lot over time. Anita explained:

In 2008, my daughter was diagnosed with breast cancer, and at the very same time of year that I had been diagnosed and at the very same age I had been initially diagnosed. At the time [of my daughter's diagnosis], I was getting an award from Angel Foundation.[13] I shared the story of my cancer and her cancer. My oncologist was in the audience. She came up to me after the ceremony, and she said, "Make an appointment with me right now."

---

13 Angel Foundation provides emergency financial assistance, education, and support to adults in Minnesota with cancer and their families.

A week later, I saw the oncologist. My daughter had the BRCA test, and it turned out that, yes indeed, we both had the gene mutation. Of course, we didn't have the test before '96, and I had never heard of it either. We both found out we are carrying the mutation, so my daughter had a double mastectomy and chemo. There was a 2 percent risk of me getting ovarian cancer, so I said, "Fine, let's just do the hysterectomy, too. Let's get everything out that could possibly be triggered by this."

The most common form of genetic breast cancer is related to a mutation in the BRCA1 or BRCA2 gene. According to the American Cancer Society, a woman with one of these mutations has a seven out of ten chance of developing breast cancer by the age of eighty. Those with a mutation also tend to develop breast cancer at a younger age than those without and are at risk for developing other cancers, especially ovarian cancer.[14] For patients who have a genetic form of cancer there is always the fear that it will come back somewhere else. There is also fear for other family members. The repeated surgeries and the constant uncertainty can be difficult to deal with.

I had genetic testing done after my mother and brother died from a genetic form of colon cancer. There was no evidence of the mutation. This was very reassuring when I developed breast cancer, as colon cancer, breast cancer, and ovarian cancer can all be part of the BRCA gene connection. Apparently, my breast cancer was random and not connected to the cancer that killed my mother and brother. The irony is that throughout their struggles with colon cancer I always maintained that I would rather have breast cancer because it is easier to remove the breasts, with less intrusion

---

14   For more information on genetic breast cancer and other risk factors, "Breast Cancer Risk Factors You Cannot Change," American Cancer Society, last revised September 10, 2019, https://www.cancer.org/cancer/breast-cancer/risk-and-prevention/breast-cancer-risk-factors-you-cannot-change.html.

into the body and bodily function. Life sometimes has a strange sense of humor.

Sometimes, family history can increase individual risk even when there is no evidence of a genetic link. Breast cancer sometimes occurs in family clusters. A cancer cluster is defined as multiple people having the same type of cancer, a rare type of cancer, or a cancer not usually seen in certain groups. The cause of the cluster may be unknown, but if a number of the members of a specific family have a certain type of cancer, even if there is no known hereditary link, then other members of the same family may be at a higher risk for that particular cancer.

Beth is part of a family cluster. She described her family history:

My aunt, who was my mother's sister, had breast cancer when she was in her thirties. Then my mom got cancer when she was in her fifties. She was in Korea at the time, and they thought it was just back problems. By the time she got to the United States, we feel in retrospect that it had been spreading. She pretty much had cancer that, even though she had treatment, they couldn't arrest it, so she died when she was fifty-five.

Then my sister got cancer when she was in her forties. She didn't have any kind of chemo. They were able to remove a very aggressive lump that didn't have any spread. It has not recurred for her.

Then I got cancer when I was in my fifties. The way that it was discovered was pretty unique. I had gone to a genetic counselor because of the cluster. They had tested my sister, and she was negative for BRCA mutation. They were saying, "You don't have a mutation, but you must have a family cluster because a lot of people are getting cancer."

Beth wanted a prophylactic mastectomy due to her family history, but the surgery was not approved. Her next mammogram showed cancer.

A personal history of some other cancers can also increase breast cancer risk. Having Hodgkin's lymphoma substantially increases the risk of breast cancer, especially if the lymphoma is treated with radiation at an early age. Kelly had Hodgkin's lymphoma at the age of eighteen and then developed breast cancer at the age of thirty-nine. She spoke about the fear that comes with a cancer history:

> They told me there would probably be residual problems from the radiation and the chemo, some of which were that I could potentially not have children and then multiple things with the radiation. Over the last twenty years, since it has been twenty years, I have always lived with the fear of getting another cancer because once you are told you have cancer . . . I don't think people who have not been there understand what it truly is to hear it.

Kelly had lived in fear of another cancer for twenty years when she developed breast cancer. The diagnosis did not take away the fear of additional future cancers; it only exacerbated it. She is now waiting for what she describes as strike three, the one that will end her journey.

The number-one risk factor for breast cancer is gender. Ninety-nine percent of breast cancer occurs in individuals assigned female at birth. The second is age. The longer a person lives, the greater the risk of developing breast cancer. The majority of breast cancer diagnoses are in persons over the age of forty, with a peak between the ages of forty and fifty. This peak is just prior to the time that many people go through menopause, when hormones change drastically.

Hormones are a known risk factor for a number of cancers, including breast cancer. Experts agree that use of hormones for contraception and for hormone replacement therapy and the rise in obesity (which affects hormones) play minor roles in the increased prevalence of breast cancer. However, newer research suggests that risk related to hormone use may be overstated and may be dependent on several variables, including the patient's age. I used herbal preparations to abate menopausal symptoms. These have estrogenic properties, but their role in breast cancer risks is unknown.

Diet and exercise habits are also potential risk factors, especially the high fat content in the diets of Westernized cultures. Fatty diet, alcohol, and lack of exercise go hand in hand with obesity and hormonal changes in the body.

Other suspected risk factors include childbearing and breastfeeding practices. Delaying pregnancy and limiting time breastfeeding may contribute to increased risk. Many women in developing countries have traditionally married and had children early in life and have breastfed their children for longer periods of time than their counterparts in more developed countries. With industrialization and Westernization, these traditional practices are changing, and cancer rates are increasing. While childbearing and breastfeeding practices may be a factor, there are likely to be others. People are living longer, which in itself increases cancer risks, but they are also often delaying childbearing and having fewer children as well as living more sedentary lifestyles and consuming diets higher in fats. This combination of potential risk factors makes it hard to single out any one factor.

Other factors that may increase risk of breast cancer include an individual's age when menstrual periods start, their age when menopause starts, their age at the time of giving birth to their first child, breast density, and weight. Other factors, such as alcohol consumption, medications, and environment, may also be contributors.

Another suspected risk factor is stress. We know that the body's immune system suffers due to stress, opening the door for many opportunistic invaders, including cancer. Carolyn received her breast cancer diagnosis shortly after accompanying a close friend through cancer and death. She is convinced that the stress related to watching her friend die was a contributing factor to the development of her own cancer.

In addition to contributing to cancer risk, some lifestyle factors may be somewhat protective, such as breastfeeding, exercise, healthy diet, and aspirin use.

Each individual has a personal risk related to the interaction of multiple factors, including family history, genetics, and environmental factors. Many of these factors and their interactions are poorly understood. Experts tell us that the best prevention is to maintain a healthy lifestyle, try to minimize stress, and be diligent with screening.

All this can be very confusing. People often think that something they did contributed to their cancer and may carry feelings of guilt when diagnosed. The truth is there are so many potential risk factors that we cannot eliminate them all, and some, such as genetics and age, we cannot affect at all. We can only try to lead the healthiest and happiest lives we can.

Despite all we know, there are still many myths surrounding the causes of breast cancer. A group of physician assistant students traveled to Tanzania to help conduct a workshop for medical professionals around cancer risk factors and early recognition. Part of the assessment of their work included a pre- and postworkshop survey of knowledge related to cancer risks. The preworkshop survey revealed that over 74 percent of participants, including nurses and physicians, believed that carrying money in your bra was a risk factor for developing breast cancer.[15] In the United States, we consider ourselves well informed, but breast cancer myths exist here too, such as bra underwires and deodorant being causes of breast cancer.

The good news is that research is helping us to learn more about cancer—how it develops and how to treat it. New screening techniques detect cancer at earlier stages, and early detection simplifies treatment and prolongs survival. Other new tests determine cancer characteristics that can simplify and guide treatment. Still others help predict likelihood of recurrence. Researchers are also helping us understand the social and emotional needs of breast cancer patients, creating resources for survivorship as part of routine breast cancer care.

RECEIVING THE DIAGNOSIS

February 4

I felt a lump today. Just a small one, maybe a pea size or smaller, but it is there. In the upper right portion of my right breast. I don't know what to do. Do I tell my husband? Do I call my doctor? Do I wait and see because it's probably nothing? I don't have a family history of cancer, so I shouldn't be worried, right? Maybe I should call my sister. I missed my mammogram last year, come to think of it. What was I thinking? And I don't know the last time I did a true self-exam. I just noticed it today in the shower. I'm kind of freaking out. It's probably nothing, though. Maybe I'll just wait a week or two and see if it goes away.

---

15 This was only one of the many myths uncovered by Tara Rick and several PA students who traveled to Tanzania to conduct a workshop on cancer risk factors and screening in 2015. Tara Rick is an oncology PA and an adjunct professor in the PA program at St. Catherine University in Saint Paul, Minnesota.

February 14

It's still there. Hasn't changed. I told my sister last night. She said I should see my primary and get a mammogram scheduled and not to wait any longer. I suppose she's right.

The scenario above is fictitious but common. Finding a breast lump starts an internal struggle: Is it cancer? Is it nothing at all? Does it warrant a medical appointment? If it is cancer, it needs attention; waiting can give it time to advance. But if it turns out to be benign, the person may feel like they were stupid for making the appointment.

After the testing is done and the results are back, it is up to the provider to break the news. How do you tell someone they have cancer? How do you bring a person's world crashing down? Provider training advises giving bad news in a quiet, comfortable place free of distractions. Patients should have a support person present because they will not remember everything. Providers should offer support without making promises they cannot keep. They should be compassionate, kind, and honest, avoiding the use of statistics that may not apply to the individual patient. They should be mindful of the patient's fears. It is important for patients and providers to remember that virtually nothing registers after the shock of the word *cancer*.

One woman told me, "I was in shock. I started shaking the minute I was told." For many, the word *cancer* is synonymous with death. You can cite statistics related to breast cancer incidence and survival rates to reassure patients, but no amount of reassurance and support can erase all fear.

There will be shock. There may be tears. There may be anger directed at the person giving the news. Providers need to remember that we are dealing with a person who is scared and in shock.

Even when we are trying to do everything right, things can go terribly wrong. Each patient has unique needs. We may not be able to understand them all.

My new patient one day was a middle-aged woman from the Middle East who had come to see me for her breast and pelvic exams. She had a male doctor who had done the rest of her physical, but she wanted a woman for the more sensitive parts of her routine exam. We reviewed her health history and completed her exam, then scheduled a routine mammogram. A few days later, I received a report from the breast center. Her mammogram had been abnormal, so she had undergone a core biopsy. I still had the report in my hand when she called to complain that the biopsy had been a traumatic event and, to make matters worse, she was having an allergic reaction to the tape used on her dressings. She asked about her results. I didn't want to tell her over the phone that she had cancer, so I scheduled her for a same-day appointment to look at the rash on her chest and review her biopsy results.

The patient arrived with her daughter. They sat side by side in the exam room and asked for the results. I gave them as gently as I could. It is never easy to give a cancer diagnosis. I was prepared for emotion, but I was not prepared for what happened next. The daughter immediately began screaming at me so violently that spittle went flying. She accused me of violating the family's wishes and disrespecting their culture. She threatened to sue. Her angry voice permeated the clinic. When I finally left the room after failing to defuse the situation, several of my colleagues were standing at the door, concerned for my safety.

What had I done wrong? I had honored the patient's request for her test results. I had presented the facts and tried to present treatment options so that she could make informed decisions. I had done everything right by the book. But I had to recognize that there are multiple factors in play when giving a diagnosis. The patient came from another country where a cancer diagnosis may have been synonymous with a death sentence. She and her daughter were afraid. I did not realize they came from a culture in which the doctor typically gave a serious diagnosis to a family member rather than to the patient themselves to avoid creating additional stress for the patient.

What this woman and her family needed was hope. They needed to have a plan and to understand that there was hope for a healthy future. Unfortunately, we could not get past the anger on that initial visit. I tried to dispel the anger with words of hope; I explained that the cancer was in an early stage and that it was treatable with a good prognosis. Those words did not register. The mother and daughter were too caught up in their fear and their anger.

Christian explained the role of hope in the face of fear. He talked about the apprehension he sees on the faces of patients who are newly diagnosed, an expression that he describes as "one of fear, dread, basically ready to write her will and dig a hole and crawl in." He described a different affect once the person has met with their provider:

> If you watch them walk out, it is a totally different experience because now they've got something to say: "Okay, I have stepping-stones to get me through this rocky water. I have a way to get through this." At least there is a plan. We really try to get people in as quickly as possible not only to see the surgeon but to see a medical oncologist because that apprehension of not knowing, that's really the downfall. That is where people have that spiral.

He also observed that the time of diagnosis is not a time to overload the patient with information. He feels the best providers are those who limit questions to three top concerns at the time of the initial visit. He recommended that when a patient receives the diagnosis, they get a notepad and write down all their questions so that they can have them answered over time. They should bring a spouse, an adult child, or someone else with them to help remember the details. They should address their top concerns at each visit. Christian recommended taking notes and reviewing online charts and results for best record keeping:

> You go into that appointment, and you just have no clue. Even with the best docs who can explain everything to you, you are going to walk out and not remember. We have a lot of upset patients who say, "I wanted all my questions answered," and later will say, "You're right. I only remembered the three things, and honestly, I barely even remember those. If I had tried to get fifteen questions answered I wouldn't have remembered anything."

> People do not understand. They think they're very educated and very smart, but your body is in a flight-or-fight response, and your brain is not firing or thinking the way it is [normally]. Emotions are overrunning everything so that logical immersion in answers just goes right out the window.

With the ubiquity of cell phones and electronic medical records, patients do not always get the news of their diagnosis in a controlled clinical setting. Some get a phone call that catches them at an inconvenient time. Kelly was away from home when she got a call that changed her life:

My phone rang, and I answered it. It was [someone from] the breast center. She said, "Oh, hi, Kelly. This is so-and-so from the breast center, and I just wanted to let you know we have your results back."

It hadn't even been twenty-four hours, so I thought that it was very strange, knowing that usually no news is good news. She said, "I do want to let you know that it did come back as breast cancer."

I don't think I heard anything else she said after that. I just lost it. I could not believe it. I was all by myself, totally not expecting that kind of a diagnosis over the phone, especially.

I think back to what she said, and I remember her saying, "This is so treatable. Some people don't even consider it a breast cancer. Don't worry. You're going to be fine." But I didn't hear that, none of that. It didn't matter to me except that it came back positive.

I went to the car and I couldn't even drive. I was just flabbergasted.

Like my patient from another country, Kelly did not hear the words of reassurance. She did not connect to the words of hope offered by the woman from the breast center. She too was overcome by fear.

Lisa did not receive her cancer diagnosis in a quiet room from a compassionate provider, either. She made the initial discovery by reading her chart online when reviewing results from an MRI done to evaluate shoulder pain:

I happened to have a friend from Florida who was visiting me that weekend. So when I got the news . . . I actually read the MRI report online on Saturday night. That's how I found out. The basic results of the MRI had some scary words . . . and I didn't really know what they meant, including "metastatic," and there was only one definition I knew of that one. My favorite words were "multiple and expansive osteolytic lesions." Those were the ones I had to look up.

My friend was there, so I was just lying on the sofa, and she was doing the internet search and reading me the definitions of those words. There was nothing we could find that was better than we thought it might be. That was a Saturday night. It was Presidents' Day weekend. . . . Monday was a holiday. But I did find out medical professionals work on holidays, so that's good.

At the time, Lisa was living far from family. She continued her story:

Now, fortuitously or coincidentally, there was a family function the following weekend back in the DC area. So I held off telling my immediate family or anybody in my family until I saw them personally. I officially was told what it was by a doctor, confirmed diagnosis after biopsy and all that kind of stuff. I actually got that word after I had landed and was on the way to pick up a rental car. The first person called while I was on the shuttle to the rental car place, and she said, "Is this a good time to talk?" I said, "You might as well tell me," and the doctor got on the phone while I was waiting for the rental car.

FAMILY AND FRIENDS

In the first stage of the journey, there is the shock of the diagnosis and everything that comes with that. A patient must simultaneously face their own mortality, manage their emotions and those of their loved ones, and learn to accept that their life is forever changed. At this point, they face the unknown with fearful anticipation of the journey ahead.

They still have to be alert and responsive to the emotional impact of the disease on those around them. Telling family and friends is hard. I was very worried about how my dad would take the news of my diagnosis; he had lost his wife and oldest son to cancer just a couple of years before. I couldn't tell him in person because he lived in another state, so I called my sister and asked her to deliver the news in person and to provide the emotional support that I couldn't.

At that time, my youngest daughter, Lisseth, was a very young single mom, and I was her major support system. My cancer diagnosis hit her hard. Her description of the day I told her I had cancer illustrates the impact that news can have on loved ones:

> I remember the day I found out. I remember knowing that she was going to get checked and thinking that it wasn't going to be that big a deal. I remember when she called me. I was taking a shower and got out of the shower, and I had a missed call from her. I called her back. I was walking through my kitchen downstairs in my town house. I was in a towel, and that's it. I called her back, and she told me that the lump she'd had checked out was cancer. I remember being on the phone, staying calm, and I asked her what they had to do. My friend's mom had just died from breast cancer, and my grandma had died from colon cancer, so I knew cancer wasn't good. She

told me that she had to figure it out. Again, acting like it was not that much of a big deal because she wasn't dead.

I got off the phone with her, and I dropped the phone on the floor. I lay on my floor in the kitchen, naked in a towel, and cried for a couple of hours or so until my son woke up from his nap. Then I had to go to work that evening. I cried and cried and cried and didn't know what to think.

I remember going to the hospital. I remember crying at the hospital. I remember seeing her at the hospital. I remember apologizing to her for dumb things I had done as a child because I was scared she might die, and I wanted to make sure she knew I was sorry for the things I had done that were terrible. I thought she was going to die, and I needed to get it off my chest.

The transition from *caregiver* to *cared for* is sometimes difficult for the patient to accept, but it lifts burdens and lightens the load. It was a friend, Sue, who walked my daughter through her fears by introducing her to healthy breast cancer survivors, letting her see that there was hope.

By the time I received my second cancer diagnosis, my daughter was a registered nurse who had worked in oncology and emergency medicine, but it was still difficult. I had surgery about a week before Christmas and was at a family gathering when I saw a missed call from my oncology nurse on my phone. I checked my voice mail and learned that the surgery had failed to remove all the cancer cells. Lisseth and I cried together over the message.

Kelly's daughter was much younger. Her reaction to her mother's cancer occurred a year after diagnosis but had no less of an impact. Kelly explained:

It didn't just affect me. It was an experience my whole family had. My daughter, last year, started having a ton of anxiety. She wouldn't go to school, didn't want to be away without me. We brought her to counseling because I didn't know what to do. I had no idea how to help her. She was so distraught. They said this was a post-traumatic stress disorder due to the cancer. With both my kids, we were very upbeat. It was very positive. Everything was going to be fine, and it was. But the counselor said that at the age she was at, it was very typical for kids to suppress their anxieties and their fears, and it tends to manifest in a year or two years for most people. Sometimes it doesn't manifest until later. For her, it was spring when I was diagnosed—it was almost the end of school when I was diagnosed, and a year later it was: "You're almost done with school. Why are you so upset? Why don't you want to go to school? Everything was fine."

The counselor told us it might have been the smell of spring. It might have been the warmth of spring. It might have been something that happened at the end of school the year before that triggered it. She didn't know why.

Kelly's daughter's delayed response is not unusual. A cancer diagnosis triggers grief. We process grief in stages, and each person will go through the stages in their own time and in their own order.

Women often take on the role of caregiver. We are often the ones others turn to when they need a rock. We try to continue that role in an attempt to protect our loved ones from the impact of the disease. Kelly had been devastated with fear when she received her diagnosis, but, like me, she tried to present the news to her family in the most positive light possible. She was upbeat with her family despite the fear, which still brought tears to her eyes when I interviewed her after her treatment was completed and her cancer was gone.

The emotional struggles of patients and family intertwine. It is no easier when cancer recurs—you revisit old fears, both yours and those of your loved ones. The day I told my adult children that my cancer had returned, my son posted the following on Facebook:

My mother is the most amazing woman I have ever had the pleasure of knowing. She may be quiet and super smart and sensible but her strength is the glue that has always held my family together. Today I was in my room watching basketball and my sister calls and says [Mom] is at your basement door knocking [and] she wants to talk to us. . . . Immediately, I knew something was wrong for her to come over and want to talk to me and my sister. My first initial thought was my father's condition has gotten worse or something happened with him. So I go upstairs and she tells me and my sister that she has been diagnosed with breast cancer AGAIN. . . . Twelve years ago she beat it and got both breasts removed hoping to eliminate the chances of it returning. Instantly my heart breaks and my eyes tear up but I try not to show it. . . . She says don't worry, I beat it once and I can beat it again! Her strength is incredible. . . . After telling me this she laughs and says don't worry. . . . I can't leave you guys to take care of your father. If anyone knows my dad he's more than a handful. Then she cracks a few more jokes and leaves. If anyone knows me I'm not looking for sympathy but I do believe strongly in God and know everything is in his hands. So what I'm asking for is PRAYERS to heal my mother and rid her of this cancer. I figure the more the better so please if you BELIEVE like I do, pray for her for me please.

Cancer pulls relationships in new directions. Roles have to adjust. Working through all the details can be daunting. Like a chessboard that is overturned, every aspect of life becomes a little more complicated. My husband, as my son mentioned in his post, has his own health issues. Due to a combination of comorbidities that include a form of dementia, he is not able to comprehend the intricacies of my treatment or their implications on our life. This may be a blessing for him, but it robs me of what should be a major source of support.

Spouses and parents often need to become caregivers for their partners and children. They may also try to suppress their own emotions to protect their children. Dick, like most of the people I interviewed, worried about his kids and the impact of their mother's illness:

> The hardest part of it was how much to tell our kids, and to bring them along in a way that was going to do the least damage to them. We chose not to involve them in every decision or in any of the longer-term speculation about what might happen. But we also needed to not wait too long.

The role of caregiver is multifaceted. Spouses, parents, and friends take on new responsibilities in many areas. The small things can be invaluable. One woman wrote in her journal:

> [My husband] has been the best helper, husband, father there could ever be. He has taken over all household responsibilities for me and the kids. He has been my best friend and support during this whole thing. I love him so much. I never appreciated before what a truly wonderful man he is and I promise to never forget it.

The caregiver needs to be strong but often struggles through an emotional journey. One husband, Roger, described the feelings of helplessness watching his wife, Carolyn, go through breast cancer treatment:

> Just seeing the vulnerability of anybody in those situations is just devastating. Even if you are not the one. In the middle of the night you wake up and look over and realize there is nothing you can do. So often you think, "I am the master of my own ship. I can do this." But when it comes to other people, they are largely like cats. You can't tell what the heck is going on with them. You just feel ineffectual . . . Everybody looks tough when they are sleeping and on chemo, but when a person is resting in that situation it's like looking at a deer sleeping somewhere. They look vulnerable and fatigued. It's just tough. It's a miserable, stinking disease.

My friend Tim told me about his experience with his wife's breast cancer. He described watching her being rolled down the hall to surgery when suddenly she reached out her hand to him. When Tim's hand met hers, she placed her wedding ring in his hand. He continued to watch until the doors of the surgery suite closed behind her. He held her ring in his hand, tracing the small circle with his finger absently as the thought entered his mind that he may have seen her alive for the last time. Then he sat down and waited.

Although patients and loved ones are all affected by the diagnosis and the changes that go along with it, those who are diagnosed with cancer often try to be stoic instead of sharing the burden. We try to be brave for one another and for those around us. We concentrate on the task at hand and try to ignore our own emotions in order to support those around us.

Barbara lost her mother and two sisters to breast cancer. She was lucky enough to have the flexibility in her work schedule to allow her to help care for her sisters when they had no one else to accompany them on their treatment journeys. She described the pain and the joy she felt:

My emotional journey has been a real roller coaster. Those six years of breast cancer with my sisters were definitely [full of] ups and downs. I was so down that they were dying, and I was so up that I could be with them and could be there and could help and that I was able to be with both of them when they died. That portion of it was really the highs and lows every other minute: "I'm so glad I can hold your hand. I'm so sad you're dying."

If you're in the position that I was in, and you're caring for someone that you love so very, very much who has any kind of cancer, stay there with them. Know that you are making a difference in their lives, whether or not it is evident. The pain that you are feeling now is not something that goes away. I have tears in my eyes now just talking about it, but the pain is balanced somewhat by the knowledge that you were there and that you helped. You did something. You held that hand, kissed that brow, lay in that bed. I lay in bed with my sisters and held them when they were dying.

Barbara was fortunate that she had the flexibility to be present for her sisters and family relationships that were close enough to allow sharing.

Strained relationships do not automatically heal—they sometimes break apart. Beth felt bad that she was not there for her mother at the end of her life. She wanted to be, but she and her father had differences that were hard to bridge. Beth's husband was going through his own health concerns, and her daughter was pregnant. It was hard for Beth to be away from home for any extended period to help care for her mother. Additionally, her abrasive relationship with her father made it difficult to be in his presence and made what little time she had with her mother uncomfortable. Her absence from her mother's last days and even her funeral are still sore spots for Beth. Time has helped, but scars remain.

Breast cancer is an emotional roller coaster for everyone involved. Caregivers can feel the effects of the experience for a long time. Dick described his own feelings while his wife, Maren, was going through treatment and how her illness continued to affect him emotionally after her death:

The emotions . . . the truly awful thing is fear. I've never, ever felt that afraid and probably never will again. The sense that you can't believe this is happening, and you can't believe you can't stop it, and you can't protect your children from it, and you can't protect her from it. I certainly would have traded places with her. I think it would have been easier for me to trade places with her than to watch her die.

My grief counselor told me something really interesting. I'm a reasonably healthy guy, and I've never really been hypochondriacal. Two or three months after she died, I had really let my guard down. I was still concerned about my children, and I started imagining bad things happening to myself. The counselor said, "You cannot believe how common it is for somebody, particularly of your age, that has lost someone." She said one of the stock questions when people show up at the emergency rooms with vague heart-attack symptoms that they can't explain is, "Did you recently lose somebody?" That's how common it is. You sort of finally let yourself break down. It took a long time before I wasn't thinking, "Oh my God, I'm going to get cancer myself," or, "I'm going to get hit by a car."

In terms of self-care, I needed to take care of myself enough to do what I needed to do. But understand that I knew this had a timeline. I think for guys in my position of caregiver with wives that have breast cancer that ultimately will survive, I'm sure it's a completely different story.

It is important for family and friends to understand that breast cancer can have a profound impact on many lives. Beyond the emotional roller coaster, breast cancer can create logistical and financial difficulties for patients and families. It disrupts lives that are often ill equipped to manage it.

Chapter 4

THROUGH THE
HOURGLASS

Sarah after mastectomy.

From "**2 a.m.**"

A cast of characters visits me at 2 a.m.
They conveniently hide during the day,
making their grand entrance only in the darkness.

After the diagnosis
Mr. Fear wakes me up at 2 a.m.
What is happening to me?
Am I going to die?

After the healing has begun
Mr. Indecision returns at 2 a.m.
Should I do reconstruction? Tram flap or implant?
How can I choose between two imperfect solutions?
Fear returns periodically reminding me . . .
People die of this you know.
What if it comes back?

—GAY WALKER

TREATMENT OPTIONS

One day, life is a certain way; then suddenly a diagnosis changes everything. The breast cancer diagnosis catapults a person into an unpredictable journey that will change their life forever. They do not know whether they will survive, but they have no choice but to go forward. They are beginning the most important race of their lives.

Each patient's experience with breast cancer is different. The severity of the disease, the treatment options, the complications, the physical response to treatment, and the emotional response are unique to the individual.

I attended a survivor event where the keynote speaker used the analogy of an hourglass. She equated cancer to the narrow part of the hourglass, where it is hard for the sand to pass through.[16] It is the time when cancer becomes a major focus that can easily overshadow all other parts of our lives. During that time, it is difficult to see into the future, to envision a life after cancer.

First comes adjustment to the diagnosis, moving from tears and fears to formulating and following a plan. There are multiple factors to consider. The type of cancer and its stage of advancement come first. There are also factors related to available treatment options and patient and provider preference. Other considerations have to do with past medical history and life circumstances, such as finances.

Decisions should always be well informed and evidence based. It is important for patients to understand the advantages and disadvantages of all options. Any decision has to be based on a combination of medical and personal factors with a goal of eradicating the cancer and preventing recurrence or metastases while providing patient satisfaction.

---

16 Ruth Bachman, https://www.ruthbachman.com/.

When I first received my diagnosis of breast cancer, I went straight to the medical literature. I found that my type of cancer, lobular carcinoma, had a relatively high rate of recurrence, even in the opposite breast. That sealed my decision. My surgeon recommended a lumpectomy followed by frequent follow-up MRIs; I opted, instead, for a double mastectomy. The surgeon and oncologist did not recommend adjuvant therapy at that time and felt that the mastectomy reduced my risk of recurrence to about the equivalent risk of being hit by a bus, so I was released from care with no scheduled follow-up. We now know that breast cancer recurs after mastectomy in 1 to 2 percent of patients. I am part of that 1 to 2 percent.

Treatment decisions have been more complicated the second time around. The potential for scarring makes lymph node mapping more difficult. Choosing which type of postsurgical adjuvant therapy to pursue is still a little bit of a guessing game. Because my cancer is hormone receptor–positive, my care team recommended radiation after surgery followed by a commitment to five years of hormone-blocking therapy to reduce the risk of the cancer returning for a third round.

Kelly didn't have a choice. Her breast cancer was in a very early stage, but she had a history of chest radiation due to a lymphoma at age eighteen. This was her second bout with cancer.

> My breast cancer was technically easy to get rid of. It, hopefully, will never come back. I had no option. I had to do a mastectomy. I couldn't have a lumpectomy, which would have been the preferred treatment with my type of cancer, but I couldn't have any more radiation to the chest, and my thought philosophy was that if I could get rid of every ounce of breast tissue so that my chances of having this particular cancer come back would be 1 percent, then I would have time to focus on all the other things that could happen. I don't have to worry so much about this.

Surgery is inevitably a part of any breast cancer treatment plan. There are two types of breast cancer surgery: breast-conserving therapy and mastectomy. Breast-conserving therapy, or lumpectomy, often couples with radiation to reduce the risk of recurrence. Its aim is to preserve the normal breast as much as possible while providing the same long-term outcome as mastectomy.[17] Despite the surgeon's best efforts, however, conserving surgery does not always preserve the normal anatomy of the breast. One woman I interviewed described her breasts after surgery as "cattywampus."

Breast-conserving therapy is not an option for some patients due to the size or number of tumors, calcifications within the breast, previous radiation of the chest (as in Kelly's case), or other concerns. For others the choice is between a simpler surgery and a more radical surgery followed often by a long reconstruction process.

There is no statistical difference in survival rates between breast-conserving therapy and mastectomy in early-stage breast cancer. However, breast-conserving surgery sometimes requires additional initial therapy and closer follow-up, including regularly scheduled imaging. Mastectomy, with or without reconstruction, does not preserve the cosmetic integrity of the breasts or the sensitivity of the breast related to sexual stimulation. The sexual changes are often not discussed during the decision-making process.

Patients may choose mastectomy over a simpler surgery because of fear of additional therapy, such as radiation or chemotherapy. Others may choose this option to avoid frequent follow-up and expensive imaging.

Many early-stage cancers can be treated with surgery alone or surgery and radiation, both of which target the cancer itself.

---

17 For more on breast surgery, see Appendix B, "What to Expect during Surgery" by Laura Blesse.

In some cases, no other treatment is needed. Sometimes, additional therapy is offered if the tumor characteristics and lymph node involvement suggest it might be helpful in reducing tumor size or spread. Additional treatments include chemotherapy, hormone therapy, and newer targeted medical therapies. Hormone sensitivity is considered a good thing because it means that the tumor(s) will respond to hormone-blocking therapy, which may have fewer adverse effects than traditional chemotherapy. Newer genome testing can help determine risk of recurrence and optimal therapy in hormone receptor–positive breast cancers.

Locally advanced breast cancers require a combination of therapies, including both targeted therapies and therapies that go throughout the body. Often these systemic therapies start before surgery and continue after surgery to give the patient the best chances of survival.

All this can be very confusing for the patient, who often has little medical knowledge related to the options presented. Patients and families have to make decisions in a relatively short period of time, often with limited understanding of what those choices entail. They often are still in shock from receiving the diagnosis. It is up to their medical providers to sort out the options and explain them in simple terms that the patient and family can understand in order to make informed choices even while they are trying to wrap their heads around the diagnosis and its impact on their lives.

Some patients rely completely on their providers for advice. Carolyn described herself as someone who needs to be told what to do and then can push forward and make it through. She credited her husband, Roger, with helping her through the decision-making and treatment process:

I think that one of the things that Roger and I did from the get-go was we did this together. I don't know how women do this without a very strong caregiver to help them get through it.

I was pretty far along in terms of my aggressiveness, so I was given the whole treatment. I don't know how other women react, but I became numb. I couldn't think. All I was doing was being brave and not being a basket case, so he took over. He found where I should go. He researched it. He called around. He got me in. He did all the maneuvering so that all I had to do was show up. If you had to do that by yourself, that whole thing crushed down upon you, and then pick yourself up and figure out how you are going to navigate through the process . . . Personally, once I had confidence in where I was going and they had a plan—and they never said, "You're going to die"; they said, "We know what to do for you"—then I let it go. I just did what they told me to do, and he took care of me.

Maren had an advanced cancer. Her treatment options were not so straightforward. Her husband, Dick, kept a CaringBridge journal where he described the difficulty of understanding and accepting the road forward. What they thought would be a sprint quickly became a marathon.

So, we are in the process of changing how we think about this. We had been prepared for a binary response . . . yes/no, good/bad, thumbs up/thumbs down. That's not how this is going to work. Dr. Y. talks about quieting it down, turning it off, taking away what it wants: estrogen.

Maren and I had it in our heads that we were going for the scorched earth approach . . . she's young and strong and otherwise really healthy, so let's go for the knockout punch. (All my hair fell out and I was up all night puking, so I must be getting better, right?) This is a different path. The analogy Dr. Y. used was that if we wanted all the lights in his office off, we could either walk around and break all the bulbs with a hammer, or one of us could find the switch and flip it. That's what we are going to do.

It will take all of us some time to get our heads around this, so let's take it slow. Maren was pretty emotional on the way home but rallied later. I'm sure she will attack the next phase of what now looks like a long-term project with the same inner strength and grace she has shown so far.

Regardless of the selected treatment option, breast cancer treatment is often a long process with many unexpected twists and turns. Each phase, each treatment has its own set of adverse effects. Each patient is different and choices have to be made between patient and providers on an individual basis.

TWISTS AND TURNS WITH SURGERY

Every treatment leaves its mark. Breast surgery was much less painful than I expected; I got off pain medications quickly. The biggest surprise and the hardest thing for me to deal with was the surgical drain that hung out of each armpit. They were little bulbs that collected bloody fluid that I had to empty each day. One even fell out in the shower a couple of times. I put it back myself. Each time I went back in for follow-up I hoped for removal. Unfortunately, I continued to have significant drainage and had to leave the tubes in place longer than anticipated. They made it difficult to wear regular clothes, and I had one oversized jumper that I wore whenever I had to leave the house. Sleeping required propping both arms on tiny pillows that allowed space for the drains to rest without pressure.

Every person's surgical experience is a little different. One woman who had extensive lymph node involvement wrote about her experience with surgery and physical recovery:

> It is [my daughter's] eighteenth birthday today!
>
> I have breast cancer and a lot of cancer in my lymph nodes. I had surgery—lumpectomy and lymph node dissection.
>
> I am recovering nicely from the surgery. My scars look pretty good and I have fairly good range of motion with my arm. I am doing daily arm exercises. I have numbness under my arm extending towards my back shoulder blade. The numb area has a funny tingling sensation. It is enough for me to always be conscious of it.

Physical restrictions after surgery can be discouraging. I sat in the house looking at the windows that needed washing, the shelves that needed dusting, and the laundry that needed to be carried to the basement and washed. I was frustrated that I couldn't do any of those things.

I didn't have any reconstruction done initially and had no plans for it. My youngest daughter was dismayed by my decision, concerned about body image, but my younger son told her that anyone who was looking at "mom's boobs" was "just wrong." I imagined that after my initial recovery I would look like a young boy with a flat chest, but I had not taken into consideration the toll of middle age. Suddenly my belly seemed larger than my chest. Women's clothing hung on my disproportionate frame while men's clothing clung to my middle, emphasizing bulges in all the wrong places. Buying clothes became a very time-consuming and unpleasant task. Buying a bathing suit was a nightmare. I had never imagined the toll my new body image would take on my self-esteem. I did not consider myself vain. On the contrary, I had always prided myself on my lack of vanity. Suddenly I was agonizing over what to wear. I hated the heavy prostheses and hid in baggy T-shirts and sweaters to avoid them. My white lab coat in clinic was my best friend, but most of my professional time was in the classroom, where I was exposed and all eyes were on me. I was continuously comparing myself to my young, full-figured students and felt mortified by my disfigurement.

No one else saw me the way I saw myself, and no one else knew how demoralizing my body image had become. My students, my peers, and my family all saw me as a courageous survivor with a positive attitude. They looked at what they perceived as my strength and didn't notice the change in my body. I felt like a fraud.

At one point, my daughter-in-law asked me whether I would ever consider reconstructive surgery. My response was an emphatic no, but as time went on, that tiny seed she had planted began to grow. Maybe my initial refusal to consider reconstruction was a stubborn denial of my own vanity, my own weakness. Maybe it was reluctance to face more surgery. Regardless, a little hope formed in my soul, and I gradually acknowledged, at least to myself, that I needed to do something about the devastating insecurity I had about my body. I had to make changes that would allow me to be comfortable in my own skin again.

Many people with breast cancer grapple with what kind of initial surgery and then what kind of reconstruction to have, if any. These are not easy decisions to make. Breast-conserving surgeries cause less deformity but often require more follow-up and screening than breast-removal surgery. Breast removal is a more radical surgery and, if reconstruction is an option, requires additional surgeries before the removal and reconstruction process is complete. Nonetheless, many people choose the more radical option, sometimes out of fear.

There are a number of reconstruction options. Annie wanted a procedure that would move tissue from her abdomen and back to her chest but was told that the type of fat in her abdomen was not conducive to that procedure. She sought a second opinion before deciding against reconstruction altogether. Annie used humor to deal with her body changes. In doing so, she found a new calling as a comedian and now has a whole routine dedicated to breast cancer.

Another woman I spoke with was tempted to listen to her fear and opt for a mastectomy. Instead, she listed to the advice of her surgeon, radiologist, and oncologist, all of whom recommended a simple lumpectomy instead.

My friend Carol Ann called me shortly after her diagnosis and asked to meet. She was considering her surgical options and wanted more information. She was doing what I had not: considering her choices carefully and thoughtfully. My thought process had been very simple. They are external, I don't need them, I don't want to be sick, get rid of them. I had neglected an important emotional component in my decision-making process.

Carol Ann was giving much more thought to the emotional impact of her decisions. I had assumed that body image would not be a concern for me; I was wrong. Carol Ann was much more in touch with the connection between mind and body than I had been. She understood the devastating emotional effects of body mutilation. I had been aware in an academic sense but somehow thought I was immune. I think that my experience has taught me to be more in tune with the psychosocial impact of disease. It gives me a little insight into the struggles patients face when they are diagnosed with a chronic illness, deal with chronic pain, or grieve a loss of body image or body function from injury.

When I was diagnosed the second time, my surgeon told me that he would have to remove my left implant to get to the cancer. The initial recommendation for reconstruction was a flap procedure, the same one Annie had wanted, which involved using tissue from the back or abdomen to create a fake breast. That procedure seemed too extreme for me. I considered having both implants removed instead but decided to find out what other options were available. I spoke with a friend who works in plastic surgery and then made an appointment with my plastic surgeon. After a short discussion, we decided that he would work in tandem with the surgeon removing the cancer and would replace the implant during the same surgery. He could not guarantee perfect results, but he had done it before and felt we had a good chance of success.

Whether reconstruction is done immediately after mastectomy or at a later time, the reconstruction process itself is full of surprises. Since breast implants sit under the muscle, the first step after mastectomy is to insert expanders that are gradually enlarged until the chest-wall muscles are stretched out enough to accommodate the desired size of implants.

At the beginning of my initial reconstruction process, the plastic surgeon explained that I would have general anesthetic to put the expanders in and then again when they were replaced by the actual implants. In between the two surgeries, I would have periodic visits to inject more saline into the expanders until they reached a size that felt right to me.

The initial surgery went well except for the fact that I developed an allergic reaction to the bandages on my chest, but after each expansion, my activities were again limited as my chest muscles recovered. I considered the expanders little more than an irritation. Right away, however, I noticed that clothes were fitting better, and my self-image began to return.

The biggest surprise came with the nipples. I had not wanted them, but the surgeon felt they were important, so I acquiesced. My new nipples, the ones I had not wanted, were in the midline of my artificial breasts—not in the lower position that is anatomically correct for a middle-aged woman. They were so high that I was worried they would pop right out of a scoop-neck top. Besides that, they were huge. I couldn't wear a regular bra yet, and they were obvious through my sports bra and anything but the thickest, loosest top I could find. The surgeon explained that while they would never be exactly in the correct position for my age, they would move down to a more natural position over time and would not always be so big. Over time, his predictions came true.

Change in sensation has probably been the biggest tradeoff. Breasts are sensual organs. Even when they are no longer perky, they are part of sexuality and sexual stimulation. I no longer have natural breast tissue with very sensitive nipples, and my chest wall has been cut so many times that even normal skin sensation is decreased or abnormal. My implants are foreign bodies. They are not sexual organs anymore. This causes some changes in bedroom dynamics.

I waited two years before reconstruction, but many women opt to do it immediately following mastectomy, often while undergoing other treatments aimed at eradicating the cancer. Other women embrace the choice to remain "flat." One woman shared her journal entries documenting her reconstruction experience.

Had an inflation (up to 400 cc each) on Monday—left breast very painful but only for three days. Today is okay. Need to get up to 600 cc each. Last one was more painful. I am going to wait six weeks for my next one.

I have planned out my next four days as if everything will be normal. I wonder how much I will really be able to do . . .

I am lying on the couch writing my notes. Last night, at midnight, I cried because of all of this. It has really been awful having to go through this again. The inflations are painful for four days and I hate how it looks. I just try to avoid looking at myself. Hopefully the final result will look okay. Otherwise this was all for nothing. I am still feeling weepy today—kind of feeling sorry for myself . . .

Later on in the process, she wrote:

Had another inflation. That was super painful: #9 on pain scale. First night I cried involuntarily because of the pain even though I was on pain pills. I had to stay home from work the next day, Tuesday, and be on pain pills. Went to work on Wednesday but had to go home early, had a very bad time ignoring the pain. By Friday it was bearable. I am never having another full inflation again. This is big enough! Next appointment is March 17 with [my breast surgeon] to see where we are at and discuss surgery . . .

Her next entry read:

Had surgery to replace expanders with implants. This was a one-day surgery and then home.

Found out I had two broken ribs from the expansions. That explains why that last one was so painful!

Breast reconstruction is not medically necessary, but it can do a great deal for self-esteem and emotional healing to help a patient move beyond the cancer diagnosis.

CHEMO AND THE BALD BADGE OF COURAGE

Surgery is often combined with chemotherapy and/or radiation, each of which has distinct and unpleasant side effects. Chemotherapy aims to kill the cancer and prevent it from spreading, but it is also poison. It kills both cancerous and healthy cells, and its effects on the body can be devastating. One woman wrote about her experience and her fears:

Entry 1

I start chemo on Friday.

I am not really depressed right now but waiting for and dreading the chemotherapy. I don't question whether I need chemotherapy—I just hope it will be able to kill all the cancer cells in my lymph nodes.

Entry 2 (One Month Later)

I survived my first week of chemotherapy. It was much worse than I imagined. I got very sick, throwing up right away when I got home. It lasted until we got a new prescription—Zofran— that night. I was super nauseated for the next three days. Plus, I was so tired I could barely move. I went to work for a few hours on Tuesday but I didn't feel good at all. By Wednesday I was a little better and then Thursday was even better. I got dehydrated and had to have an IV on Friday. After that, I felt much better.

My nausea is pretty much gone but I still don't have much of an appetite. I have had a headache and backache all day today.

My mood is okay. I know I have to get through this so I take each day as it comes.

Entry 3 (Two Months Later)

The next three chemo sessions got worse and worse. I became more nauseated and dehydrated each time. I ended up in the hospital to take my fourth treatment. That helped so I didn't vomit or get dehydrated. I was in the hospital for four days.

During the treatments I experienced some excruciating stomach pains due to the dehydration and constipation. I became scared a couple of times and got so depressed I wanted to quit. There was at least a week during each session that I became very depressed and angry about the whole thing. I cried all the time.

I also got mouth sores during the second weeks so I couldn't eat or talk. . . .

I have lost fifteen pounds so far.

Entry 4 (Sixteen Months Later)

Found this [diary] while I was cleaning out drawers.

The [new chemo] sessions were not any easier. I ran a dangerously high fever each time: 104 degrees. So bad my doctor ended up canceling my last session.

I handled going to radiation every day for six weeks. That ended a year ago today. I didn't burn too bad—my skin tolerated the radiation but I got very tired and worn out.

It is hard to believe it's been a whole year. So far no other cancer has shown up. I am going to request a total round of scans & stuff every year so I can catch it before it spreads.

Her diary entries speak to many of the adverse effects related to chemotherapy. Many women fear the nausea, vomiting, and hair loss that are commonly associated with chemotherapy, but there are other, less commonly known dangers. Chemotherapy attacks the immune system. It kills off white blood cells that protect the body from infection. This can result in a dangerous situation called neutropenic fever in which fever may be the only symptom of a serious, even life-threatening, infection.

Chemotherapy not only targets fast-growing cancer cells but also affects other cells in the body that tend to reproduce quickly, such as cells in the digestive and reproductive tracts, blood, nails, and hair. These acute effects account for the nausea, fatigue, and hair loss that are commonly associated with chemotherapy.

Chemotherapy is typically administered in cycles of three to six months that allow the body some time to recover between treatments. It works best when there are few interruptions in the cycles, but sometimes adverse effects such as anemia or infections mandate treatment interruptions.

Many of the short-term effects of chemotherapy are treatable. Antinausea medications are one adjunct treatment commonly prescribed for patients receiving chemotherapy.

There are other, more long-term problems related to chemotherapy that are difficult to treat and can be permanent, such as fertility problems, bone loss, and eye problems.

The badge of chemotherapy is hair loss. Hair loss is not physically painful, but it is one of the most obvious effects of chemotherapy.

I heard a woman telling her breast cancer story on a radio program. She talked about losing her hair during chemotherapy and the challenge of deciding whether she was a "scarf woman" or a "wig woman." She felt that the scarf was more transparent and honest, but it was also depressing. Every time she looked in the mirror or saw her reflection in a window, she saw a sad, sick woman staring back at her. She saw this reflected in the eyes of others as well. They all looked at her with pity, "as if they were about to cry."

The wig would let her hide a little. Perhaps people would notice it was a wig, but it would signal them to be discreet, to not ask how she was doing. They would know she did not want to talk about it, and they would keep quiet even though they realized why she was wearing the wig. She wanted to be a scarf woman, to be strong enough to be open and honest about her cancer, but it was not easy.

Chemotherapy-induced baldness is a physical sign that makes it impossible to find solitude, to go unnoticed. Patients without hair can't always choose whom to share their journey with; the effects are visible to all. Patients can try to keep it private by wearing a wig and can discuss it only with those who need to know, or they can wear scarves or bare scalps in public and show the world that they own the changes cancer has made. The bare scalp and the scarf signal acceptance of not only the physical changes but the emotional changes as well.

Change happens in stages. The woman on the radio gradually accepted her hair loss and the depression that it brought her. The hardest part for her was when her eyebrows disappeared. The scalp was only her head. Her eyebrows were part of her face, part of who she was. When they began to disappear, she felt very vulnerable. That was when she decided to try a wig. Other people I have talked to resorted to eyebrow tattoos.

Whether or not to wear a wig was a common theme among the people I interviewed. For some, baldness was not a huge issue. For others, it was a constant reminder of their disease. It made them feel exposed and vulnerable.

One woman described her decision this way:

I'm not a pink-ribbon girl. I wore a wig the whole time because I saw that if I wore a scarf, people just looked at me with pity. The wig, they don't know for sure. I put on a lot of lipstick.

Many talked about head shaving as a milestone. One woman described it as a relief:

I lost my hair around November 10 or so and had it shaved. The losing the hair part was much harder than actually getting it shaved. It was actually a relief to get rid of it and not worry each day if big clumps would be missing. The wig doesn't bother me, and I get a lot of compliments on it . . .

The woman on the radio tried a wig, but the wig didn't last long. Other people echoed her experience. One woman shared her thoughts:

I thought I needed to get a wig. That was the worst thing ever. I hated it. I thought, "Why did I buy this stupid thing?" I would prefer a hat or nothing. I know there's a big stigma about walking around bald, but now I see women walking around bald, and I wish I would have done that. There's no shame in it. I was sitting in the radiation waiting room, and this older couple was there. We started talking, and they were asking me if I was losing my hair and if I wore a wig. I told her, "Don't even bother with the stupid wig." Be proud and just go out there.

Her experience was similar to that of another woman who told me this about her experience:

I couldn't even wear a wig. I hated it. It itched, and it felt uncomfortable, so I would wear my scarfs to work. I would always go and work that third week after chemo, just before the next one. I remember I would get so hot because I was on chemo that I'd have to get the scarf off my head. It was like a pot of boiling water that I had to get the lid off. I'd be in the back room with my coworkers saying, "Can I take off my scarf?" They said, "Of course," so I went to my boss and asked, "Do you mind if I walk around bald? Because I can't wear this all the time; it's too hot." No one looked at me differently, being bald. I didn't even know I was bald. That's how comfortable they made me feel. No one judged my bald head. It was really neat.

Another common theme had to do with support and celebration. Head shaving often became a way for friends and family to come together and create solidarity around cancer treatment. One woman told me:

I didn't [make my head shaving a party]. My friends did it. We went before I even started the treatment. It was a gathering. It turned a very sad occasion into a [celebration]. . . . It was very nice.

Another woman shared her thoughts on head shaving:

When I got my head shaved, I went with my mom and my sister. A friend of mine had a party, and everybody gave her a hat. I thought, "Why didn't I do that?" I thought I would be so upset, but it's not bad. I had the bald head in the summer, and it was so nice to go swimming and not have to worry about hair. I put a ball cap on, and it was fine.

It was actually kind of cool. I have a college-aged son. He and my husband both shaved their heads too. That was kind of fun as a show of support. Then everybody started to say, "Are you going to do the [Susan G. Komen] 3-Day? Are you going to do the Walk for the Cure?"[18] I'm not a crowd person. I decided I would leave that to other people.

It kind of connects you to a whole community. You're part of the club. All of a sudden you have this connection. It was so amazing to find so many people who had a similar story. They went through the biopsy, and they went through the diagnosis. It's really eye opening. It really does make you appreciate your good health and your good fortune . . .

One woman I interviewed, Connie, is a hairdresser and said her own experience with baldness changed her approach to women with cancer who come to her salon to have their heads shaved. When she received her breast cancer diagnosis, she drew on her faith and asked God to use her experience for others. She now uses her own experience with chemotherapy and the compassion she gained to make the experience less stressful for clients. She makes head-shaving visits a celebration. One woman who came in to have her head shaved had two teenage daughters, so Connie gave her a mohawk and took pictures, creating a light, fun experience and some good memories before shaving the hair off. She made it her mission to bring joy to those who are suffering. If a woman wants a wig, she has a lot of new knowledge to share and even offers to go to the wig supplier with the woman. She was embarrassed that she never realized, until she had breast cancer herself, what emotional turmoil women were going through when they came in to have their heads shaved.

---

18 The Race for the Cure is a three-kilometer walk or run, and the 3-Day is a sixty-mile walk over three days. These events bring together breast cancer survivors and supporters and raise money to support research to reduce the number of breast cancer deaths.

Connie has a new mission in her work. She sees the beauty in the individual, whether bald or with a full head of hair, and makes it her duty to help her clients see their inner beauty as well.

TARGETING WITH RADIATION

Besides chemo, the other common cancer treatment is radiation. Radiation may occur before or after surgery and is often combined with chemotherapy as part of the treatment plan.

Radiation therapy targets the breast or lymph node and does not have as many systemic effects as chemotherapy because it does not go through the entire body. Radiation therapy can reduce the rate of recurrence by up to 70 percent. It is helpful in all stages of cancer, even in metastatic cancer. Radiation can be part of a sequence of treatments that may include any combination of surgery, chemotherapy, and/or hormone therapy. Fatigue is the most common side effect. Skin reactions are also common and may resemble sunburn symptoms, such as redness and blistering. Other potential adverse effects include low white blood cell count, which increases risk of infection; chest or axillary pain; and shortness of breath. Radiation may also increase the risk of heart disease later in life.

When I received my second breast cancer diagnosis, there were a lot of questions surrounding the optimal treatment. My first surgery had failed to remove all the cancer cells that had spread to the muscle; a second surgery cleaned up the margins, but the question of residual cells or chances of recurrence remained. Because hormone receptor–positive cancers don't respond as well to chemotherapy, my oncologist decided on radiation for my adjuvant therapy.

Monday through Friday for four weeks, I went to the radiation oncology department for my fifteen-minute treatment session.

The radiation technicians and doctors carefully marked out the radiation area. They even drew a target on my breast and took multiple pictures of the correct placement.

Each day when I arrived, I dressed in a pale-green robe that I removed at the start of treatment. My arms and head went into a custom-made mold to hold them in the correct position. The technicians secured my feet with a large rubber band. They then moved the table into position and adjusted it until the target on my breast was in the exact position the radiation oncologist had specified.

In order to protect my heart, the machine delivered radiation when I was holding a deep breath so that my chest wall was away from my heart. This was a little tricky. If my breath was too deep or not deep enough, the target did not line up correctly, and I had to try again. It took two or three perfect breaths to do the job. There were usually some imperfect ones in between.

The first day of radiation, I went home and took a nap. After that, I did better. I still felt fatigued in the mornings and in the evenings but continued to work through the entire four weeks. Other than some mild redness and swelling in my breast and some muscle soreness in my left arm, overall I did well.

On my final visit with the radiation oncologist, the doctor advised me that symptoms might get worse before they got better, which they did. The fatigue seemed to intensify the week after treatment ended and lasted for several more months. The redness and soreness also got worse and took weeks to resolve. Several months after treatment, I still had some pink color to my left breast along with my left foot being more red than my right.

My radiation oncologist recommended hydrocortisone cream with aloe to prevent skin thickening and scarring. He advised me to continue it for three weeks after treatment. He also had me use deodorant with no metallic ingredients during radiation treatment. His nurse recommended several brands that did not contain aluminum or titanium, common ingredients in many antiperspirants. My dentist prescribed a special toothpaste with extra fluoride to protect my teeth from the effects of radiation and the follow-up hormone-blocking therapy, both of which are hard on the bones and teeth.

Both radiation and chemotherapy affect the immune system and put patients at risk for infections of all kinds. These infections can be difficult to detect because the body's natural immune responses, such as fever, may not occur as they would in a person with a healthy immune system. Patients and providers alike need to be vigilant to prevent infection and to detect signs and symptoms before they become serious.

SMOKE FROM ANCIENT FIRES

When my friend Ruth Ann was dying, her family was desperate. Conventional therapies were not working, and she was going to die if they couldn't find some alternative therapy. Her sister started researching and found something in Mexico that looked like it could be promising. They knew they were grabbing for straws, but they didn't see any other source of hope. They never had the chance to try the new treatment, however. Ruth Ann died before her sister could make the necessary arrangements to try the new treatment.

A complementary therapy is a treatment used in conjunction with more traditional Western therapies such as surgery and chemotherapy. These may range from music therapy, acupuncture, or medications to control pain and to counter the adverse effects of treatment to herbal supplements and special diets that boost the immune system. More and more oncology practices are seeing the benefit of complementary therapies in providing holistic and patient-centered care. Complementary therapies can treat aspects of the cancer experience that traditional medications cannot touch or soothe the adverse effects of caustic cancer treatments. Alternative therapies, meanwhile, are nonstandard treatments that are used instead of conventional medical treatment. Together they constitute the group of therapies referred to as complementary and alternative medicine (CAM).

Complementary and alternative medicine encompasses a number of modalities, ranging from prayer and meditation to herbal medicine and acupuncture. Some of these have a long history of use and can be helpful. Others can be harmful. Unfortunately, despite some advances in research, there is still not widespread understanding of CAM therapies by Western medical providers. Many are not even comfortable discussing alternative therapies with patients, though others incorporate them into their practices on a regular basis.

Oncology is an area where complementary and alternative therapies have made a foothold. Many providers recognize that certain foods and herbal preparations can be helpful for the side effects of chemotherapy as well as related problems, such as sleep disturbances and stress. Other therapies, such as yoga, meditation, and music therapy, can be very helpful in managing the fear, stress, and depression that are all part of the cancer journey.

Providers need to be able to talk to patients about CAM even if they don't know a lot about the specific therapies and modalities available. They need to be able to listen, advise, and assist patients in finding the resources that they need. If the medical team doesn't provide accurate information in a nonthreatening way, patients may seek out CAM alone, without understanding interactions between CAM and Western medicine or the limitations and dangers related to some alternative therapies. Providers need to help patients find a safe way to incorporate a multipronged treatment plan.

Some cancer centers provide counseling, support groups, music therapy, and even acupuncture clinics. Many oncologists are knowledgeable about alternative treatments for nausea or make referrals to nutritionists who can help. Pharmacists can be helpful in finding information on specific herbal products to make sure that there are no interactions or contraindications that would make them harmful to a specific patient. A comprehensive care team can provide a comprehensive approach to cancer care that is both acceptable and beneficial.

Despite the growing knowledge and use of CAM by providers, many patients do their own research and make decisions on their own. The internet is full of recommendations, making it difficult to sort through all the information and find what is appropriate for any individual. There are some basic principles to observe.

The first rule of medicine is nonmaleficence, or "do no harm." Many complementary practices can be very helpful for problems associated with cancer and have little or no potential to cause harm. These include options such as meditation, music therapy, acupuncture, and massage, which not only help with stress but can also help the individual cope with pain, nausea, and depression. It is important to find a practitioner who has plenty of experience, particularly experience with cancer patients, in order to maximize the benefit.

Many herbal products can also be helpful but should be used with caution and in consultation with a knowledgeable herbalist or other provider. "Natural" does not always equal "safe." Herbal products are pharmaceuticals, and they have similar safety profiles to prescription medications. It is important to understand the indications, contraindications, and adverse effects as well as any possible interactions with other prescribed therapies. Some herbal products may interfere with chemotherapy or other cancer treatment or may even be carcinogenic, meaning they can cause cancer.

Besides just knowing what you can take, it is important to know how much you need to be effective and how much is dangerous. This is difficult with herbal products. Herbals are considered dietary supplements and do not have the same oversight and regulation as prescription medications. Many over-the-counter herbal preparations are not what they seem. Some are contaminated or mixed with other products, even antibiotics or steroids. The strength of the product may also vary from brand to brand or even from bottle to bottle. They may lose efficacy if they sit on the shelf too long or if climate and other growing conditions were not optimal.

Patients trying to research complementary and alternative therapies face a daunting task in finding reliable resources. Many turn to the internet, where there is a plethora of information, but most of it is anecdotal or in the form of advertising. Very little information on sound, objective research is available. The National Cancer Institute provides some guidelines for finding reputable sources. The agency recommends checking websites to determine their purpose: Who runs the website? Do they have a commercial interest, such as selling the product? How old is the information? Is the research biased or is it based on opinion? What was the research behind the recommendation? Is it free of commercial bias?

Books and articles can be equally biased and misleading. They deserve the same level of scrutiny as websites. A medical provider or pharmacist, even if not personally knowledgeable about CAM, can help find reputable resources. Most pharmacies have research-based resources that can be helpful when considering an herbal preparation.

Despite all the precautions and warnings, CAM modalities can be very useful for breast cancer patients. Many of our modern medicines are based on ancient herbal knowledge. Scientists have studied some ancient Egyptian and Chinese therapies, done additional research, and created modern therapies based on ancient practices. Some of these discoveries have revolutionized cancer treatment and support of cancer patients.

CAM modalities can decrease the need for harsh prescription medications as well as provide invaluable support through a very difficult time. The patient needs to choose carefully and enlist help in sorting through the options in order to choose the safest and best modality for individual needs.

As Western providers explore the world of complementary and alternative medicine and practitioners of the ancient medical modalities learn more about Western research methods, the two worlds are beginning to cooperate in research. The resulting collaboration is starting to produce medical breakthroughs and better knowledge on how to both treat cancers and support cancer patients through their difficult journeys.

Breast cancer care now often occurs at a cancer center that recognizes the holistic needs of survivors. These centers are much more likely to provide patient-centered team care. Professionals from a variety of different health and wellness fields can evaluate and meet the specific needs of a given patient. The team leader works with the patient to determine the makeup of the team and when each member's services are needed. Services provided might include physical rehabilitation, mental health services, nutritional counseling, spiritual health, lymphedema care, and/or social services as well as a variety of additional CAM options.

Chapter 5

COMING OUT THE
OTHER
SIDE

The 3-Day walk, 2007.

From "**Healing Shelter**"

After time has healed your hearts
and mended broken wings,
inventory honestly life's most important things.
Questions only you can know
the answers to so well
can set you free forever
from your own private hell.

You are stronger than you know
for you've survived this war.
And still inside have courage
to stand and take no more.
No longer are you victim,
for now you have control.
So take what you have learned here
and liberate your soul!

—JULIETTA CHEVALIER

WHEN TREATMENT ENDS

Eventually, the treatment sequence ends and the patient is free of scheduled treatments. This should be a time of jubilation, the end of the journey, where the hourglass widens and the sand falls through effortlessly. This is the beginning of survivorship. It is also the beginning of the transition from the life that was to the life that is to be. The pace begins to slow.

The hourglass analogy is an appropriate one. The thin part of the hourglass is the active phase of cancer treatment, or the sprint. It is a narrow path, very hard to travel. It is where cancer's intrusion is the most impactful. Cancer care teams understand how hard it can be.

Often during my radiation treatment, I noticed candy, pastries, or other small gifts set out with the coffee and water that were always available to patients and staff. I assume that the treats were gifts from patients finishing treatment to the staff who had cared for them. The staff made the daily visits to the radiation department pleasant. They were cheerleaders for patients dealing with serious illness and unpleasant treatment. They added a little fun by placing a cutout of Waldo on the ceiling above the radiation bed and moving him periodically so that we could play "Where's Waldo?" during treatment. At the end of treatment, they gave out graduation certificates and smiling congratulations. The small gifts were symbols of patient appreciation for their support during difficult times.

Once we are past the point where treatment ends, we come out changed forever. The sand exiting the narrow part of the hourglass looks the same as it did in the top, just as the cancer survivor may have few outward signs of all they have endured and learned. But they have scars under their clothing and other changes that are even less obvious to the casual observer.

Once the treatment is finished, the breast cancer patient is left in a state of limbo somewhere between sick and well. Most of the symptoms related to the cancer and its treatment abate, but nothing is as it was before. Friends and family congratulate the survivor and return to lives that remain just as they were before cancer. They expect the survivor to do the same, not realizing their world and their life have changed.

Tara, an oncology physician assistant, talked about the post-treatment needs of the breast cancer survivor:

> The thing that I have found profound and interesting is that people would, time and time and time again, come back afterwards and say that they thought it would be great when they got to stop chemotherapy and be done and not have to come back and see us as often but that it was like cutting the umbilical cord. It is really, really difficult for people. They felt kind of lost during that period. They looked forward to coming back and seeing us. Something that had been, maybe at first, something they dreaded, then later it became something comfortable.

Focus shifts from the next cycle of treatment to "Who am I now?" It is often when a survivor feels most alone. Their treatment journey is over. The medical team that supported them through treatment is no longer a part of their regular routine. It is as if the people who truly understand disappear. These people are no longer a part of the inner circle. The patient is starting a new stage of the journey—survivorship—and it can feel very lonely.

I attended a seminar on survivorship that included a panel of cancer survivors. Each one had a different story, but all of them talked about the changes that took place in their lives and their difficulty trying to return to a "normal" life after treatment. They talked about needing time to adjust to a new life. Some found solace in support from other survivors. Others just wanted to be left alone at first, needing time to adjust before being able to accept support from even those closest to them. Some were haunted by worry. One survivor said, "Life is hard. How you live your life is in your control. Live today. Living in fear is not living at all."

Beyond the emotional and physical impact of cancer and cancer treatment, there are logistics of life that cancer turns upside down. Connie described her survivorship care this way:

> I met with the survivorship program three times: before, during, and after my treatments. They have an electronic survey, and then they take that electronic device after you've answered the questions and they plug it into the computer and it spits out a chart, like a diagram of where you need assistance, where you need help. They use that to gauge where you are at in your physical, emotional, financial, spiritual—all those areas—and then they have resources. Wherever you are lacking, that's where they fill in the gaps with resources.

Ideally, survivorship services should start early, before the end of treatment when the person is feeling lost in their new identity. Newly diagnosed persons need to know that the end of treatment is not the end of the cancer journey. Life will not automatically and immediately return to the precancer normal. It will take time to discover the new normal and settle in to a new identity that feels ill fitting at first. The marathon is not over yet.

LONG-TERM EFFECTS

Carolyn talked briefly about life after cancer. She felt that she had gotten off easy but still had residual effects:

> One thing I did after was hire a personal trainer because I had had the whole thing, the surgery, the chemo, the radiation, and the lymphedema. I felt like I had lost it all. Being physical is a huge part of who I am—I told my counselor the other day that I would rather go for a walk than have a piece of chocolate cake.
>
> I had lost all confidence of who I was during the chemo process. A friend of a friend [of mine] knew someone who had gone through breast cancer and had lymphedema, so she was aware of how lost you get. She came to my house. It was a huge investment, but it was something I needed. I had no balance, I had nothing, and she brought me back to a very good place, but the first time she told me to stand on one leg I fell right over. You lose all of that. That's the thing you go through that nobody will give you an answer on. I asked all these caregivers, "What can I do? What can't I do? What's best, what's not?" Finally, Dr. Y. said, "Exercise never hurt. Always exercise."

Carolyn's experiences with aftereffects of cancer treatment are common. All treatments have potential lasting effects. Regardless of the treatment regimen, adverse effects can occur and continue after treatment is complete. Some resolve shortly after treatment is finished, and other residual effects are long-term. It is difficult to predict the long-term consequences of breast cancer treatment.

While advanced screening often discovers the disease before it is symptomatic, the treatment is physically and emotionally devastating, often leaving permanent physical changes and emotional scars.

Following treatment, survivors find themselves with new problems they never anticipated. Chemotherapy can cause infertility and early menopause or menopausal symptoms. Other side effects might involve bone or muscle pain, weight gain, and fatigue. Physical scarring and other changes occur after both surgery and radiation as well. These changes are not only a blow to self-image but can have an impact on sexuality and relationships.

Emotional changes such as anxiety and depression are common. The phenomenon of "chemo brain," or chemotherapy-related cognitive dysfunction, can also both be frustrating and interfere with a person's ability to function normally. Many of the survivors I interviewed complained about lingering chemo brain. It can last long after treatment and can interfere with function in a variety of ways, including forgetfulness, trouble concentrating, trouble multitasking, and taking longer to finish tasks. Forgetfulness can involve memory lapses, trouble remembering details such as names and dates, or difficulty with word-finding. It can come and go and disrupt multiple aspects of life. Some potential causes of chemo brain–type symptoms include cancer, surgery or anesthesia used during surgery, chemotherapy, and other drugs used as part of cancer treatment or treatment of side effects. Other illnesses or comorbidities, age, and emotional issues such as depression or stress may exacerbate cognitive changes.[19] Many of the factors that cause chemo brain may interact at the same time and may continue long after treatment ends as the survivor adjusts to post-treatment life. Organizational aids, such as list-making, may be helpful. Adequate

---

19 "Chemo Brain," American Cancer Society, https://www.cancer.org/treatment/treatments-and-side-effects/physical-side-effects/changes-in-mood-or-thinking/chemo-brain.html.

sleep and exercise are important. Social support and counseling can help with emotional components.

Lymphedema—swelling that results when blockage in the lymphatic system prevents lymph fluid from circulating normally—can be a late effect of either surgery or radiation. Lymphedema may occur in the arm, breast, or leg and can involve extensive swelling. It usually develops gradually and may start with some tingling or numbness before swelling is noticeable. Early treatment is important.[20] Josh, president of LympheDIVAs, a company that makes compression sleeves for lymphedema patients, noted that people who have had both axillary node dissection and radiation have the largest amount of risk. Somewhere between 25 and 50 percent of people who undergo lymph node dissection develop lymphedema, and the risk remains for up to twenty-five years after surgery. Even if someone only has a sentinel node biopsy done, like I did, they're still looking at a 5 to 15 percent approximate risk.[21] Josh recommends using a compression sleeve during travel and other sedentary times even if you have not had a history of lymphedema in the past.

Chemotherapy and hormone-blocking therapies can cause menopausal symptoms, such as hot flashes and sleep disturbances. In addition to being annoying, these effects can be hard on the bones and teeth. It is important to check bone density for thinning before osteoporosis develops. Thinning bones are at higher risk for fractures from even minor trauma. A good diet, supplements of calcium and vitamin D, sunshine, and weight-bearing exercise can protect and improve bone health.

In all these ways and more, breast cancer treatment is a life interruption that can continue well after the end of treatment and can make resuming previous activities challenging.

---

20 "Lymphedema," breastcancer.org, https://www.breastcancer.org/treatment lymphedema.

21 Information provided by Josh Levin. Learn more about Josh and LympheDIVAs in Part 3.

LITTLE THINGS THAT MAKE LIFE BETTER

Body image can be a confusing mix of love and hate. Women and girls are especially vulnerable to insecurity related to physical appearance. Society indoctrinates little girls with a societal norm for a woman's body. It starts with Barbie dolls and similar "girl" toys. Our pretty dresses and our hair are the subject of compliments rather than our intellect or abilities. We are totally immersed in the princess culture from an early age. It teaches us that how we look equates to who we are. All this makes puberty a stressful time for girls' body image. Body changes make us self-conscious and unsure of how to accept our own new reality or how others will accept us. Our bodies are our temples, or so we are told. However, the architecture of that temple is always changing, mirroring the events of our lives and our interactions with humanity.

A disease that challenges perceptions of femininity and attractiveness can have a negative impact on self-image just as much as puberty can. Regardless of the type of treatment, it changes the appearance of the body and can throw us back into that pubescent state of body image distress. The survivor is no longer "Jane." She is "Jane with cancer." The body changes related to cancer treatment label the patient like a flashing billboard, or at least it feels that way in our own minds. Many want to hide the changes, to look more "normal." We go through painful reconstruction or other procedures, or we accept ourselves in our new reality and cope.

Annie had a mastectomy to treat her cancer. She explored options, but in the end she decided against reconstruction. Her changed body did not go unnoticed. She described one encounter:

I have a big belly. What I did not realize was that it really is only the belly that is big; my tush, legs, arms, and face are not big at all. This said, after my breasts were removed, my tummy was very distinctive. It looks like I am pregnant. One day as I was helping out at my son's school manning the front desk, a parent comes in and asks me when I was due. Now I get this and other pregnancy questions a lot. I told her I was not preggers and explained my story. Later that day, flowers arrived at the school for me as an apology. I generally do not, but this time I got a bit ticked off. Don't send me flowers; send me money! I can get over money. After that, I signed up for stand-up comedy classes. I have to find the humor in things or I would break down. I have also found that when I share my humor, others who need it understand and appreciate it, and it helps them get through their low points.

We each need to find our balance in what is acceptable to us in terms of our relationship with our own bodies. Our scars can be a source of shame or a badge of honor.

Some people embellish with tattoos. Tattoos vary from enhancing reconstructed nipples to covering scars. Some expand across the chest like a garment. Tattoo artist Trent Wyczawski specializes in breast tattoos for people who have survived breast cancer. He recommends that a survivor wait a minimum of five months (preferably a year) following treatment before getting a tattoo and find an artist who has had advanced training in breast cancer–related tattoos. Breast tissue is delicate, and surgical scars will change slowly over time. They need time to heal completely for the best artistic results from tattoos. Radiation also thickens and burns skin. Some of those changes will never heal completely. Older people have thinner skin over the breasts than younger people, and inexperienced artists can damage their delicate skin.[22]

Emotional scars are equally in need of healing. Emotional support needs to continue through the healing process, long after treatment is finished.

Carolyn talked about a friend who knew how to provide quiet support through her chemotherapy and beyond. The interview took place five years after Carolyn's diagnosis. She was still receiving daily texts:

> I get a text every morning that says "Good morning, sunshine" from a very dear friend. She started sending that to me the first day I went to chemo, and I think she is afraid to quit. So Roger and I would be sitting at the table. Our heads are down and I'm trying to eat and there's a phone tinkle, and we both smile at each other because it is my "Good morning, sunshine." She would bring us cookies every Friday on the porch because that was my chemo day, and Monday she would bring a pot of soup. Every Friday. Every Monday. She wouldn't come in. She would just lay it on the porch. Those kinds of things will be in your heart forever.

---

22 The complete interview with the Firefly Sisterhood and Trent Wyczawski is available at https://soundcloud.com/user-298534622/to-tattoo-or-not-part-2-tattoo-artist-trent-wyczawski-1.

Chapter 6

AFTER EACH HILL,
ANOTHER
APPEARS

3-Day breast cancer walk, 2006.

From "**Hills**"

After the purchase of a new Schwinn bike
I am aware of hills.
I never noticed how many there are
until cycling uphill.
Little ones hardly noticed
Surprise my new bike legs.
Each hill an effort to climb.
Huffing and puffing
I become the little train that could.

[. . .]

Breast cancer has been my steepest hill.
I have crested it and found healing on the other side.
Rhythms and cycles
Challenges and healing.

Always another hill to climb
just as I thought I was finished.

—GAY WALKER

RECURRENCE RATES

When I first received my diagnosis, I rushed to the medical literature. I wanted to know about my type of cancer: What were my chances of recurrence? What was the best treatment option for me? It wasn't that I didn't trust my providers; I just needed to weigh everything myself so that I could consider my choices before I actually had to choose. As a medical provider myself, I was very familiar with reading medical literature and deciphering the meaning, and I approached my diagnosis from my usual point of reference—that of a provider, not a patient.

Armed with my own research, I was ready to propose options that would tailor my treatment to my preferences. I was prepared for the decision-making process. I opted for a double mastectomy to minimize my risk of recurrence and to avoid frequent screening and unending worry.

After my mastectomy, I had several follow-up appointments with my surgeon. When my drains were finally out and my scars were healing well, he sat down with me to discharge me from his care. Since my cancer had been small and my lymph nodes were unaffected, my surgery was considered a cure. He told me that my chances of recurrence were about the same as being hit by a bus. He went on to describe symptoms that would warrant follow-up: jaundice, weight loss, unremitting fevers, bone pain—all symptoms associated with metastasis. I had one follow-up visit with an oncologist, who also dismissed me as cured. Good. I was done.

After that, I thought I was breast cancer free, but a little voice in the back of my head spoke up every time I had a symptom that could possibly signal metastasis.

Fast-forward eight and a half years. My interim journey had been unremarkable. I was sixty-four years old and had developed low back pain that radiated down my legs, causing cramping and making it difficult to walk. I also noticed a pain in my right chest when I lifted weights. Ordinarily, I would have tried to work it out with exercises, but in the back of my mind I could hear my surgeon's words: "Bone pain." I felt like a fool for worrying, but I would have been more of a fool if I had ignored important markers that the cancer had returned.

I couldn't help but think about the worst-case scenario. What if it had metastasized to the bone? I knew what that meant. The prognosis would not be good.

My mind raced. My life insurance was tied to my job, so I would need to keep working. What would my husband do? I was the one who handled the finances; that had never been one of his strengths. What about my dad? He was ninety years old and lived alone. What about my kids? They were all grown, but . . . the thoughts raced on. What would I look like without hair? I had to make the appointment. I had to know.

I wasn't fearful of the outcome. I was more fearful of the unknown, the uncertainty. I knew I could handle whatever was ahead—at least, that's what I thought, but I had to know. I have a habit of playing scenarios over and over in my head, like acts in a play or speeches to be written. I could deal with reality, but I wanted the mental scenarios to stop. I wanted to have something concrete so that I could make a plan.

I went to see my primary provider. She felt compelled to investigate even though we both thought everything would turn out fine. It did. A bone scan and several MRIs later, I was several thousand dollars poorer and still in pain, but I was cancer free. I was reassured, for the moment.

The whole experience made me think about the words we use. Until then, *survivor* had been a word I used without thought. Now I wonder whether there is a better word. How can you call yourself a survivor when the threat of a recurrence is always hanging over your head? My online thesaurus provides *stayer, sticker, fighter,* and *toughie* as synonyms for *survivor.* None of these fit right either. The first two imply that one chooses to stay, but this disease is not a choice. You could argue that we are fighting to stay in this life, fighting for survival in a fight that never really ends. Some people use the word *thriver,* but that doesn't really fit all the time either. Sometimes we thrive, and sometimes we don't. Is there a better word? We need one that encompasses many aspects of the journey. It must convey fear as well as the strength to endure. It must include the pain and devastation caused by treatments as well as the love and support that often bolster us through the process. The word must also encompass the end of treatment and the uncertain, often rocky road of ups and downs that comes with a disease that is never completely cured. Such a word is beyond my vocabulary. The closest I can come is the analogy of a marathon.

I was lucky that I had dodged the bullet . . . that time. My cancer would return twelve years after my original diagnosis. According to my surgeon, I am one of the unlucky 1 to 2 percent of women who have a recurrence after a mastectomy. I tried to find statistics on breast cancer recurrence rates, but there are a lot of variables. These include type and size of the original cancer, lymph node involvement, whether or not the cancer has spread locally to the chest wall or other organs, treatment, time elapsed since the original diagnosis, and more. I found several online recurrence risk calculators, but none of them included enough variables to give a dependable risk assessment. This confirmed what I already knew: that breast cancer is a complex and unpredictable disease. We can never rule out the possibility of recurrence.

WHY IT COMES BACK

The second or third time around can be disheartening and very frightening. Kelly talked about her fear of getting another cancer after surviving first lymphoma and then breast cancer. She explained:

> This breast cancer was very simple, all things being said, compared to most. But I think what was hard for me was that I kind of had this notion of: I had a cancer once. It was a good cancer. I was diagnosed at a midstage, so I had a pretty good chance of surviving it. I did. Then this one! Now it's still that survivor fear of what is next. This, I feel, is probably a stepping-stone. There is probably going to be something else in my future. But if you can stay on top of it and be your own advocate, hopefully you'll catch something early and be able to treat again.

Later in our interview Kelly became tearful talking about the constant threat of another cancer hanging over her head. She survived lymphoma as a teenager. She was told that she would probably never be able to conceive, but she did. Twice. Now she has also survived breast cancer. She knows she has been lucky; she has dodged the bullet twice. That doesn't take away the worry. She knows the next time is likely to come. She knows her luck may run out. She also knows she is at higher risk for other related problems. Her oncologist is watching her cardiac health because of her history of chest radiation and the increased risk that can cause for heart disease. She has a good life, but it is never completely free from fear. She is always waiting for the next chapter in her cancer story. She knows that the race is not over.

Anita's initial diagnosis of breast cancer was in 1983, when she was a young mother. In 1986, she decided to have reconstructive surgery, and in the process another lump was discovered, found early, and removed before it could spread. Her story was not over yet:

> I assumed everything was going to be fine, and for ten years it was. I was talking to someone who was a twenty-year survivor but had had a recurrence after twenty years, and I thought for sure I was clean since it had been ten years, and my impression was that that meant I was done. As soon as I heard her story that twenty years later there was a recurrence, I said, "Okay, that's it. I need to go back and get everything checked." So I went back to the doctor, and I said, "I need to double-check about whether or not this is something that would go away or would come back again." The doctor said, "I don't know if I made that clear, but you are never cancer free with breast cancer."

It wasn't until her daughter was diagnosed with breast cancer in 2008 that Anita learned her breast cancer was genetic. Patients with positive BRCA1 or BRCA2 genetic cancer are at higher risk for other cancers, such as ovarian and colon cancer. Anita ended up having her uterus and ovaries removed to lower her risk of related cancers.

Another woman with an altered BRCA gene was cancer free for six years. In August of 2009 she wrote:

> I found a lump on my right breast when doing a monthly exam. I called my doctor's office, and they got me in the next day for an ultrasound and mammogram. Since both of those showed the lump, I was then scheduled for a biopsy. That was done on

Tuesday. No problem with the biopsy since the lump was large enough and easy to get to. The lump was at the six o'clock position. It was roughly an inch in size. They called the next day to say it was cancer.

I called the kids, my mom, and [my] sisters to tell them, "The breast cancer [is] back." That was really hard to do. Especially the kids. The surgeon recommended a double mastectomy.

Fifteen months later, after completing reconstruction and six sessions of chemotherapy, she wrote:

I had another surgery two days ago. This was to take out my uterus, ovaries, tubes, and cervix . . . The reason for the surgery is preventive because of my breast cancer . . .

I was nervous about this surgery and the recovery. I am angry that I have to disrupt my normal life and then start all over again. I am really sick of not being healthy!

I have not heard about the pathology report on everything they took out. Hopefully no cancer cells.

All three of these women had underlying risk factors for recurrence, either a previous cancer or a genetic type of primary breast cancer, but lack of risk factors does not preclude recurrence. It is an ongoing worry for any survivor.

Breast cancer recurs when cells that were part of the original tumor are not detected during treatment and begin to grow later on. This is not a treatment failure. The treatment for the original tumor aims to kill all cancer cells, but it can miss some. These tiny cells, along with cells that were resistant to the original treatment, can lie dormant for many years before something triggers them to grow.

Breast cancer recurrence can be local, regional, or distant. It is local when it occurs at or near the site of the original cancer. Regional cancer develops in the lymph nodes near the original cancer. A distant recurrence, or metastatic disease, occurs when the lymph nodes or blood carry the cancer cells to body organs farther away, such as the bones, the liver, or the lungs. Younger patients and those who have lymph node involvement or a larger tumor are at higher risk of recurrence. A tumor that is removed goes to a pathologist for evaluation. If the cancer comes close to or is right at the edge of the specimen, it is more likely that cells will have been left behind.[23]

When I discovered my most recent lump, I had surgery to remove it and the section of muscle it had infiltrated. The cancer cells came right up to the edge of the pathology specimen. This worried the surgeon; he was afraid he had not removed all the cancer, so we scheduled a second surgery to remove a little more.

Some types of cancer are more likely to recur than others. Inflammatory breast cancer and cancers that are not responsive to hormone-blocking therapy may be more likely to come back.

Breast cancer has many relatives, including ovarian cancer, lymphoma, and colon cancer. These cancers either increase the risk of breast cancer or may come after certain types of hereditary breast cancer.

Besides the worry of recurrence, there is the stress of ongoing care. For some patients, such as Anita, there are more surgeries. Recurrence of breast cancer, metastatic lesions, or related cancers can necessitate additional surgeries. The emotional cost to patients and family is immeasurable. Breast cancer survivors often live full

---

23 "Recurrent Breast Cancer," Mayo Clinic, https://www.mayoclinic.org/diseases-conditions/recurrent-breast-cancer/symptoms-causes/syc-20377135.

and productive lives, but those lives are forever changed. There is always a perpetual dark cloud overhead. Often the sun shines through, but the cloud never disappears.

DIFFICULT TREATMENT DECISIONS

As survival rates increase, so do the rates of recurrence. Years ago, cancer was a death sentence, and it was rare for someone to survive breast cancer long enough to have a recurrence. Now people are surviving much longer, and experts are learning more about recurrence. They are also learning more about targeting treatment of specific types of cancer. Despite all the new treatment options and new knowledge, however, recurrent breast cancer can be challenging to treat. Kelly's postmastectomy reconstruction was complicated because of scarring from her previous chest radiation. My surgeon was unsure whether he could trust lymph node mapping for assessing spread due to scarring from my previous mastectomy. There is no cure when the cancer has metastasized to other parts of the body. Treatment becomes more of a guessing game and a balance between what therapy can keep the cancer at bay and what can maintain the best quality of life for the time remaining.

Chapter 7

WALKING DOWN THE
ROAD
AWAY

The author with Annette (seated, wearing a hat) shortly before her death.

From "This Is How I Will Remember You"

This is how I will remember you: sitting at the bonfire on an August
night, the stars in the sky like sparks thrown from your hands,
scattered. Your face tanned and narrow and eyes lit with flame.
I will remember your hands and your feet and the slope of your
shoulders as you walked down the road, away . . .

—EMILY ARNASON CASEY[24]

---

24 See Emily Arnason Casey's short story about her aunt who died of breast
cancer in its entirety in Appendix B.

MAKING MEMORIES

I recently came across the obituary of someone I knew long ago who died from stage 4 breast cancer. The obituary described how in the last fourteen years of her life, she never "battled" cancer but rather "added a side car to her motorcycle, inviting cancer to come along" as she continued to live her life to the fullest extent possible. It went on to describe how she went trout fishing during the last week of her life, "an oxygen tank beside her no more cumbersome than a cooler of beer." Those memories of good times, even good times laced with pain, will always be a comfort to those she left behind. Her family will tell those stories over and over through laughter and tears.

Even though death is an inevitable part of life, it can be painful for those left behind just as it is for those who experience it firsthand. Memories help ease the transition for both the dying and their loved ones. Death is a thief; it steals precious time, cheating us out of time together. The proverbial "bucket list" is one way to steal back some of what would otherwise be lost. Continuing to live to the fullest extent possible keeps hope alive—not the hope against death but the hope that life can still be beautiful. It creates memories that live on and comfort loved ones.

WORDS TO REMEMBER BY

We carry our memories of our loved ones in our hearts. Time heals, and memories fade if they are not reinforced by repetition or documentation. Generations come and go never knowing the story of the life that ended too early.

During my mom's long journey with cancer, I bought her a journal and asked her to write down memories, thoughts, anything that she would like to pass on. She never did. I wish that she had. Her life was full of adventure, pain, and loss. She had stories and wisdom that I would have loved to preserve and pass on. Most of my grandchildren never met my mom. They have no stories of their own to remember her by. She is lost to them except through their parents' vague memories or stories that I tell.

I recently heard about something called a legacy letter. It is an inheritance of history and wisdom for future generations, a gift from the heart. Many of us do not even know the names of our great-grandmothers, much less the details of their lives and the lessons they learned through experience. What a gift it would be to know their stories and to be able to cherish their words of wisdom and bits of advice. A legacy letter lets the writer determine how they want to be remembered. It gives them power over their own story. It also lets them pass on lessons learned in their lifetime, a kind of ethical will.

I gave part of my mother's eulogy and talked about some of the amazing things she did in her short lifetime and some of the important life lessons she taught me. Afterwards my sister, who is eight years younger, commented that I had talked about things that she had not known. It was as if those eight years between us had been a lost generation. I can only wonder how much more Mom could have preserved if she had written in her journal or left a legacy letter.

Even before the actual time of death arrives, it is ever present. We begin the grieving process before death comes. We start cherishing memories and worrying about how we will hold on to them. When Dick knew that his wife, Maren, was dying, he found himself unable to sleep. He kept thinking about how he would honor her when she died. Finally, he got up and wrote down what he would say at her memorial service. Then he could sleep. Our words are sometimes the only thing we can offer in an attempt to make things better, to make some sense out of something so senseless. It is our way of easing our own pain and somehow makes us feel we have eased the pain of the dead.

A GOOD DEATH

Death is part of life, but it is a part many of us shy away from as much as possible. We like to pretend that somehow we can avoid it or think about it later. But it is unavoidable and inevitable. For those with cancer and those who care for them, death seems to be creeping up from behind, making them look over their shoulders every day.

Easing physical pain and easing emotional pain are equally important as death approaches. Planning can be the difference between a "good death" and a "bad death." It is something we all should do while we are healthy, but it is even more important for those facing a life-threatening condition. Filling out an advance directive is a start. This legal document spells out who should make medical decisions if the patient can't and what specific medical interventions the patient would or would not like. Some advance directives also include more specifics and details.

When my friend Sharon's cancer metastasized to her bone and brain, she was virtually alone, so I became her caregiver and her health-care proxy. Part of that process was helping her write her advance directive. We did it with a hospital social worker during one of Sharon's hospitalizations while she still had the mental capacity to tell us what she wanted. It turned out to be a beautiful experience for both of us.

I had expected it to be a very frightening discussion of intubation, feeding tubes, and cardiopulmonary resuscitation. Instead, it was a friendly chat about what was important to Sharon. She wanted to be comfortable, at home, and with her dog as long as possible.

I was able to care for Sharon in her home for some time after that. A hospice nurse managed her pain and checked on her needs as well. Then one morning I arrived to find Sharon sitting in her living room. She looked at me and said, "I don't know where I am, and I don't know who I am." The brain metastasis had advanced. Sharon lived the rest of her days in a nursing home, where she had the twenty-four-hour supervision she needed but was surrounded by her own things and was even allowed beer when she wanted. There were no hospital heroics.

Advance directives are helpful in providing a "good" death for the patient, but there are other advantages to them as well. With an advance directive, the patient's family knows what the patient wants, lifting some of the burden of end-of-life decisions. An advance directive is also helpful for medical staff, giving them insight into what they should do or not do. Without direction by the patient, they are obligated to try to save the person's life even if they know their efforts are probably futile.

Since Sharon's death, I have had the opportunity to discuss advance directives with a number of patients. My last family practice was in a community of immigrants and refugees, many of whom had cultural beliefs around death and dying that were quite different from mine. Some cultures consider even the mention of death taboo.

Cultural beliefs like these can make discussion of advanced directives a little more challenging, but I have found that cultures that refrain from mentioning death also tend to prefer death with fewer heroics. This preference offers a compassionate way to talk about directives. I introduce them as a way to prevent unwanted medical interventions when the patient becomes unable to express their wishes, a way of making culturally appropriate choices.

Discussions with family and friends are important at the end of life. Too often people die with things left unsaid. When my mom died, she had an opportunity to say something to each of her children and grandchildren. She found the courage and strength to smile and joke and hug. My children still have warm memories of gathering around her bed just prior to her passing.

My mother told me once, shortly before her death, that it was her love for her family that kept her alive. She also told me, in one of her darkest moments, that she had never shared with anyone how much pain she had really endured. She had hidden it from us all. She was ready for the pain to end.

She and my dad had already discussed her wishes and had made all the arrangements for her death. I remember her looking at all the faces gathered around her and commenting, "This dying is not so bad." After that, she closed her eyes and went to sleep for the last time.

Part of what made her death a "good death" was hospice care. Hospice can begin at any time once life expectancy is six months or less. It can occur in any one of a number of settings, including home, a long-term care facility, a hospital, or a hospice facility. Hospice allows patients and families to customize their end-of-life experience free from avoidable pain and with the support of a knowledgeable care team. It also provides services to support the patient's family through the illness and even after the patient dies.

Watching my mother die with grace and dignity made it easier for me when I was diagnosed with breast cancer. I was able to look back at her example and reassure myself that I could do the same, if necessary.

It is important for loved ones as well as the person dying to experience a "good death." Those left behind need healing and closure. When a loved one dies, it is important for the surviving family and friends to memorialize them.

HEALING

Grief is a funny thing. It can sneak up on you when you least expect it.

I cried at my mother's memorial service and then did not cry again for a long time. My grief remained buried until about a year and a half after her death, when I was traveling in Namibia and attended a Lutheran church service. The singing was beautiful, and many of the hymns sung that day had been favorites of my mom's that I had heard her play on the piano throughout my childhood. Suddenly, there in a church in a foreign country, the dam broke. An uncontrollable torrent of tears poured down my face.

I recently heard a grief counselor talk about the grieving process. Her advice was to throw away the notion of stages of grief—we do not all go through all the stages or go through them in the prescribed order. Grief will hit you when it hits you. Something that reminds you of your loved one or an event in your life that has an empty space because of their absence can trigger a grief reaction. It will be your own unique experience, unlike any other, and it will be over when it is over. Perhaps it is never really over. The pain and emptiness may improve over time as life goes on, but the lost loved one is irreplaceable.

Dick blogged about his wife, Maren, on the second anniversary of her death.

November 27, 2012, 5:40 a.m.
Maren died two years ago today. I looked back at what I wrote that day earlier this morning:

Maren died this morning at about 7:00, at peace and surrounded by her family. The sun was coming up on a cold winter morning, and she was ready to go. The boys were here, loving her to the end.

A sad day for all of us who loved her so much.

It's hard to think about how shattering and awful that day was. Even so, it's heartening to think about where we are two years on . . . mindful of her memory, grateful for her love and her life, moving forward as best we know how. I'm completely sure that's what she would have wanted: *remember me, take care of the boys, get on with it.*

Getting on with it can be difficult. The death of a loved one hits us in ways we never expected and changes us forever.

Part 2

OXYMORONS:
FINDING THE UNEXPECTED
SILVER LINING

From "**Is It a Dichotomy or an Oxymoron
That Turns into a Paradox?**"

*Mortality aside, it was "bittersweet" at the least,
if you can't quite make the above claims.
What else can be said when death blows its
sweet/sour breath in your face
Filling your lungs with desire
to breathe in one molecule of oxygen at a time
and set each moment on fire.*

*People want you to "act naturally,"
like you ran over a speed bump
instead of a cliff.*

*Hegel understood dichotomies
like fear and freedom
scared to death
free to live
synthesis from
the mutually exclusive
to an uncomfortable juxtaposition
changing from a dichotomy
to an oxymoron and settling into a paradox
as you
live with cancer.*

—MORRY EDWARDS

Chapter 8

RELATIONSHIP WITH
SELF

The 3-Day Wizard of Bras.

From "**Healing Shelter**"

Welcome to our humble home,
a shelter from the rain.
And temporary refuge
from unnecessary pain.
Where broken hearts and battered wings
and anger, fear and shame
can find some quiet comfort . . .
you don't have to explain.

—JULIETTA CHEVALIER

SAVORING THE JOURNEY

Euphoria! Sarah rang a symbolic bell at the end of treatment. She wrote:

Ring the BELL!!!!
It may seem like a trivial thing, but believe me, it is symbolic of making it to the end of a part of this journey that I am very glad is behind me! I would not have been standing there without all the love, support and prayers we have had from everyone.

I took a selfie holding my certificate of completion when I finished radiation treatment and happily posted it on Facebook, but despite the euphoria of finishing treatment, transition can be frightening and isolating. It is like returning from extended time in another country where the culture is vastly different. The traveler immerses in the new culture and, in the process, changes their perspective and way of doing things. Upon the traveler's return, home seems different. Home has not changed, but the traveler has. The new culture has become familiar, making the old one less comfortable.

Just as extended time in another culture changes personal perspectives and even preferences, the breast cancer journey does the same. The survivor is not the same person who began the journey full of nervous anticipation of the unknown. They have faced the unknown and changed in ways that are uniquely their own, ways that others cannot always understand.

Sarah referenced the Bible, using her faith and her reliance on God to guide her through the transition.

I will lead blind Israel down a new path,
guiding them along an unfamiliar way.
I will brighten the darkness before them
and smooth out the road ahead of them.
Yes, I will indeed do these things;
I will not forsake them.
Isaiah 42:16 (NLT)

Breast cancer catapults patients into a new reality. An avalanche of emotions and concerns overcomes them as they learn to deal with visible and invisible changes.

The physical changes are constant reminders of the transformation. They may be the first thing that the patient has to deal with. Gay Walker wrote about taking an important step by revealing her mastectomy scars to her friends.[25] Their positive reactions and support helped her appreciate the impact of breast cancer on other aspects of her life.

Buddhism encourages people to experience each moment to its fullest, to be mindful of each movement of the hand, of each breath taken. Each step is a meditation unto itself. In a Buddhist tea ceremony, the preparation and the pouring of the tea are ritualized. Once the tea is poured into the bowl, it is important to observe the color and aroma of the tea. As it enters the mouth, the Buddhist practitioner will observe the effect of the tea on the tongue, the palate, and the throat and will even meditate on the tea entering each cell of the body.

Just as the Buddhist reflects on the tea's journey through the body, patients with breast cancer observe the changing architecture of their lives as the cancer journey permeates each aspect of it. They watch as their bodies change. Reflection expands

---

25 See the poem "Baring My Soul" in Appendix A.

their awareness. Each step of the journey, though difficult and painful, is an opportunity for meditation, reflection, and growth.

As in the tea meditation, the patient remains acutely aware of each step of the journey in order to balance the pain of the journey with the wisdom and compassion gained through experience.

Awareness of mortality can add vitality to life, allowing one to live more fully in the present. This is the oxymoron of breast cancer.

GROWTH FROM ADVERSITY

In part 1, I introduced the symbol of an hourglass as a representation of life with cancer. In this analogy, the narrow part of the hourglass symbolizes the most difficult part, the time of transition. This visual is from Ruth Bachman, who wrote about it in her book about her experience with cancer.[26] Once all the sand has passed through the narrow part, the hourglass is turned over, and a new life begins. Ruth refers to cancer as a powerful and profound teacher, perhaps the thing that helps us to be who we were meant to be.

When I heard Ruth talk about the hourglass analogy at a survivorship event, the part of the image that stuck in my mind was the sand. Reaction to sand is an interesting phenomenon. It is abrasive. It is also a creator of beauty. Sandpaper smooths away rough spots and renews old furniture.

Sand enters the oyster shell by accident. The tiny grain irritates the tender surface of the oyster's interior. In order to protect itself, the oyster forms a smooth, protective layer around the foreign body, creating a beautiful and valuable pearl.

Cancer enters our bodies in a similar way. A DNA mistake creates rapidly dividing cells that are foreign and deadly to our body. We lack the oyster's innate ability to isolate the invader.

---

26 Bachman's book, *Growing Through the Narrow Spots*, was awarded a 2014 Midwest Book Award in the Inspiration/Gift Book category by the Midwest Independent Publishers Association.

Instead, we use surgery and strong poisons to kill it. What natural protection we possess is more emotional than physical. We have the unique ability to analyze and to learn from adversity. This ability can transform the cancer experience into something that makes us stronger, wiser, and often more compassionate. When our heart feels pain, it grows in its capacity to understand pain and to love others who hurt. When we feel a connection to another person, our capacity for compassion grows as well. Experiencing cancer, our own or a loved one's, creates an awareness of the pain of others and helps us to add a layer of love and compassion. In the end, cancer can help us form beautiful and valuable pearls.

When something bad happens in life, when someone is facing a narrow spot in the hourglass, we try to make sense of it. We ask, "Why did this have to happen?" or "Why me?" Perhaps part of this questioning is the process of healing, part of turning pain and sorrow into action, part of using the irritation of the sand to grow and transform. It is a time to make a choice: bury your head in the sand or lift it high and carry on with life in all its beauty and its pain. A survivor is someone who is living with, through, and beyond cancer.

SHARING THE PEARLS

Breast cancer survivors, family, and friends often slowly reinvent themselves. The sense of loss and confusion, like the sand, can become a thing of beauty, but the transition takes time and patience. Patience is a gentle relationship with self, a loving and forgiving relationship that lives fully in the reality of the present. Patience allows the present to heal the past. Kelly, who counsels many patients and grieving survivors, remarked that if you live too far in the past you will be depressed, and if you live too far in the future you will be anxious. We need to find peace with the present.

For some who experience cancer, patience brings about life changes in very big and unexpected ways. Many of the people I interviewed talked about those changes.

For Connie, who is a hairdresser, it changed the way she cared for her clients with breast cancer. She learned how to ease their experience with hair loss, how to make it less traumatic and more fun. She became involved with Angel Foundation and became a major fundraiser.

Annie branched out into comedy and even created an entire routine around breast cancer. Finding humor in her story was helpful in her own healing process but also provided support for other women who were dealing with their own cancer. Emily wrote a short story about her beloved aunt who died of breast cancer. Diane founded a faith-based survivor's group that has become a very large part of her life.

Gay, who wrote many of the poems featured in this book, dedicated herself to art therapy and found a new career. Carol Ann was already a social worker and a practitioner of holistic health when she joined the cancer center, but her own experience with breast cancer shortly after starting her new job added new perspective that has made her work more meaningful for herself and the patients she serves.

My own experience, too, has made me more aware. At first, I didn't know what to do with it. I tried fundraising events and survivorship celebrations and came up empty. I did breast cancer awareness talks for the Sage Program. At the time I was working in a family-practice clinic that served a large number of immigrants and refugees. With the help of the medical interpreters from the clinic, I spoke to women from a number of different cultures. Many came from countries where they had not had access to breast cancer screening. Each of my attempts to reconcile my own experience fell short by itself, but cumulatively they added to my understanding and my healing. Being present for friends and patients has also helped me to process my own experience and to heal.

In retrospect, I can see that my initial experience with breast cancer was a pivotal point in my life. It enhanced self-awareness. I learned to recognize my weaknesses as well as my strengths and to accept myself without apology. I am more in touch with my mortality and more accepting of it. In a way, that awareness is liberating. I know that I have physical scars and that I will die, but I have faced those things, so now I can let go of my fear and my self-consciousness. I can move on. Facing death makes me more aware of the absolute value of life and of making the most of it. It puts things in perspective and makes it easier to deal with things that previously might have seemed overwhelming.

My self-awareness took years to develop. My journey, though initially a relatively easy one, has been full of bumps and absent of moments of epiphany. I will continue to evolve and to find my place in my new reality as I discover my own pearls and figure out how to share them along the way. The marathon is not over.

Chapter 9

FINDING SUPPORT IN THE
COMMUNITY

The author with students, friends, and family at a breast cancer event.

From "**Prayer for the Ministering Women**"

*Our dear friend Mary, a woman of small stature and large heart,
has come home to her cabin in the pine trees to begin a process of
transformation. The doctors say they can do nothing. It appears
that her body is growing too small and frail to tether such a great
rambunctious spirit to this earth much longer.*

*And so the midwife women come, as they have since time began,
expressing with imperfect hearts and hands a perfect divine love.*

*Comes the nurse woman, gifting with bottles
of many-colored pills, anointing with a gentle touch.*

*From far away comes the childhood friend,
bringing memories no one else can share.*

*Comes the organizer with calendars and lists in one hand
and a phone in the other. She gives of her time.*

*One comes enveloped in soapy steam and the scent of bleach and
lemons. With strong hands, she smooths freshly laundered linens
on Mary's bed. She dispenses laughter.*

*The kitchen magician comes. With her wooden spoon, she can
transform humble ingredients into the most exotic, succulent dishes!*

*The quiltmaker brings her pieces of colored cloth, tosses them
into the air, and catches them in the most beautiful arrangement.*

Another can grab pictures out of the thin air and show us to ourselves.

*Gardener woman plunges her hands into the dark secret earth
and brings out flowers of brightness and beauty.*

*One comes bearing a fragrant loaf of freshly baked bread.
She has kneaded her life force into it with her passion.*

—MARY LANDRY DECKER

THE LITTLE THINGS

Many of the people I interviewed commented on friendship during their cancer journey. They noted that cancer teaches you who your real friends are—that some people get it, and some people don't. The people who get it are the ones who help without being asked, who drop everything on their busy schedules to lend a hand when needed, the ones who are simply present. One of my former students came to my house and helped me weed my garden. She understood the importance of showing support by just showing up. That small act of kindness is something I will always remember.

Sometimes the little things mean the most. When I was recuperating from my initial surgery, a coworker gave me three books from Alexander McCall Smith's No. 1 Ladies' Detective Agency series. They were light reading, just what I needed to pass the time and keep my mind engaged but not taxed. Little gestures like that mean so much. A couple of weeks after I received my second diagnosis, flowers came to my house. They were from a friend of my son's. He was one of many who had been in and out of our house throughout childhood and adolescence. I had lost contact with him over the years except for an occasional brief conversation at various gatherings, but when I thanked him for the flowers and mentioned my surprise, he told me how much our family had meant to him growing up. It was a good reminder that the little things can have a huge impact.

Lisa talked about how important cards were to her:

As a result of the diagnosis, there is a lot more gratitude that I feel or at least that I'm trying to be more expressive about. I think you become much more empathetic. You recognize that everybody has their things they are dealing with. I have always wanted to be there for somebody else when they're dealing with things, but I've never really known how to do that or how important that is.

I got tons of cards from people after I got my diagnosis. It was amazing. It was absolutely amazing. A couple months afterwards my mother was visiting, and she likes to clean. I had cards everywhere. She was going to go straighten everything up. She asked, "Is there anything I can't throw away or can't touch?" I said, "Do not throw away any of these cards." I'm not a sentimental person. Birthday cards: don't waste your money. I don't need any cards. But these cards were so important to me. Eventually I went out with some folks and we found, at IKEA, a picture-hanging wire thing, and I had three rows of them. My dad hung it up for me, and I took a picture of the cards and put it out there, and I still have every single one of them. I don't keep any other cards, never have, but I just couldn't throw them away. It made me realize how important something like that can be for somebody. It doesn't matter if it's right away or two months later, or sometimes it came on a particularly hard day. They're awesome. Realizing that you need to do that for other people and how important that can be is something I learned.

I, like Lisa, am learning about gratitude. I am more cognizant of the small things that people do for me and of their expressions of support. I am also realizing that some of the support I am receiving is the fruit of small things I have done for others, often without realizing that I was making a difference in their lives. This realization makes me more determined to show appreciation and to find small ways I can lighten the burdens of those around me.

People often shy away from the person who has cancer, not knowing what to say or fearing they will say the wrong thing. Patients and caregivers are equally guilty of using silence instead of openness, thinking that others don't want to hear or not wanting to burden friends and family. In reality, it is when we are simply present with each other that we do the most good.

The problem is that often we don't explicitly express our fears or feelings. Instead, we adopt the vocabulary of war. We talk about "strength" and "fighting" and cue others to do the same. In trying to protect our loved ones from our fear, we often lock them out, when what they really need is to be let in. By talking about our fears or simply being together, we support one another. A hug or a pat on the arm can convey empathy when there are no words.

The fear is only a small part of the journey. We need support just to face the day-to-day struggles of treatment and recovery. This is often when the little gestures and the continuing solidarity of friendship can mean so much.

Humor is a great healer. Laughter is as cleansing as a good cry. Finding humor in my experiences, being able to laugh at myself, has been very helpful. Friends who are willing to laugh with me are invaluable.

In much the same way as breast cancer patients need support, our families and friends need support too. Dick, Roger, and Tim, husbands of breast cancer patients, all spoke of the vulnerability they witnessed and their own helplessness and inability to protect their loved ones. They also talked about the support they received from friends and family, support that lightened their load during difficult times.

Carolyn flew to California to be with a friend who was dying of cancer. She lay beside her on the bed and held her friend's hand as she died. Even though it was a highly emotional time, it was also a time that was precious to both Carolyn and her friend. That experience gave Carolyn strength through her own cancer journey.

The experience of being with my mother and brother through death and my own cancer journey were invaluable when I became caregiver for my friend Sharon, who had metastatic cancer. The many little tasks involved in her care never seemed like a burden. I could do them with joy even when she was no longer able to appreciate them.

My experience taught me the value of showing that I care. I understood how lonely it is to face fear alone. When my friend Annette received her diagnosis, she lived in another state. I knew her well enough to know that although her faith was very strong, she was afraid, and she would not be able to share her fear with those close to her. I wanted to be there to hold her hand or her head, to cry with her, to laugh and share memories with her, to give her an outlet for all the emotions hiding under her brave smiles. I only had one brief opportunity to see her before her death, so I could offer support only through email and prayers through most of her journey. That one visit allowed me to be present in person, to hold her hand in silent solidarity, to express love.

While friends and family are the foot soldiers of the care team, medical providers are an important factor. Support can come from a medical professional who is able to provide an opportunity to share fears, a moment to listen, or a badly needed kind word. Several of my interviews touched on the importance of trust and confidence in the oncology care team. Carolyn changed doctors until she found one who won her confidence. Her husband, Roger, commented that even the appearance of the providers was important. He noted that the group Carolyn completed her care with all seemed happy and physically fit. That gave him more confidence as well.

There is more to being a good provider than just looking good. Oncology providers I interviewed offered clues to success. First, they have to put the cancer journey into a broader perspective; it is important to recognize the cycle of life. Tara, an oncology physician assistant, put it this way:

> Birth and death are two of the most important parts of our life. A lot of people really enjoy being a part of the birth process. It's that way with the death process too. It's a sad time at the end of somebody's life, but it is inevitable for all of us. It is also good to have people who can help ease you through that process. That's not just specifically for death.

She went on to talk about the personal stories that make her patients unique and special to her. Part of being a good provider is caring for the whole patient, not just the disease. It is important to understand who the person is and what their needs are beyond just the medical treatment.

Christian, director of the Jane Brattain Breast Center, noted the importance of hope. In his view, hope comes from having a plan. A plan lessens the fear of the unknown that is so much a part of the breast cancer journey. Patients I interviewed echoed this theme: once they found a medical team they trusted, they put their heads down and followed the plan, never looking back or wasting energy on questioning the what-ifs. Of course, plans may change over time, depending on the outcome of treatments and the progression of the disease.

Medical team members need to keep in mind that little things often mean the most. Attention to detail and to the individual patient's needs and preferences is important. Team members need to remember that the cancer is a disease, but it is not the person.

Focus must remain on the patient behind the disease. The medical team needs to help the patient and their loved ones cope with the effects of the disease on their life. No one person can provide for every need. Breast cancer care is a team effort, with the patient at the center surrounded by family, friends, and dedicated medical staff, all of whom need to support one another and work together.

My current care team includes five physicians, a nurse manager, and some very special friends who just happen to be medical providers. It also includes every receptionist, nurse, and technician involved in my care. Their smiles and reassurance make medical visits and procedures bearable, even pleasant. It has been very reassuring to know that the breast cancer care team meets weekly and collaborates closely. It is also helpful to have friends who understand and care.

THE COMMUNITY NOBODY WANTS TO JOIN

A person newly diagnosed with breast cancer joins those of us living with the disease. We form a unique community built on the shared experiences of fear, pain, and sickness. Despite our numbers, we often feel isolated and alone.

Initially I felt like an outsider in my new role as breast cancer survivor, even somewhat guilty that I had been so lucky. I had a bad case of impostor syndrome. I did the Race for the Cure and the 3-Day walk sponsored by the Susan G. Komen foundation, but those events felt foreign to me. There was no sense of belonging; I had been given a title that didn't seem to fit. People who had suffered immensely or who had lost loved ones following a devastating disease surrounded me. I had only a vague concept of their suffering. I was healthy despite my diagnosis. I had lost dear friends, but I had escaped. My group membership was shaky. I felt like an outsider looking in.

I didn't feel like part of the community until friends started coming to me with questions as they too were diagnosed with breast cancer. I started to realize that even though I had escaped many of the horrors of treatment, I was still part of a new family. By holding my friend Annette's hand and responding to emails, I provided a different form of support than what she received from family, friends, and church members. I was part of the club that understood.

When Carol Ann asked me to have lunch with her shortly after her diagnosis, I wasn't sure what I could offer. We talked a lot about surgical options. She was giving careful consideration to all options and wanted to understand how each would impact her life, her self-image, and her fears related to cancer recurring. She wanted to know all about my own choices and whether, in retrospect, I had any regrets. Beyond the details of treatment, she needed support from someone who understood. I was a survivor, a medical professional, a friend, and, most importantly, part of the community she had just joined, a select group of people who understand and can provide support.

Kelly also came to me for information and support. She was a coworker, but we never talked about cancer when we saw each other in the clinic. Kelly had decided to keep her diagnosis private as long as possible, so she contacted me via Facebook to ask for support. Our sisterhood was a kind of secret society that operated far away from the public eye. It was a network of survivors connecting informally, in secret. It taught me that I could help others by listening, sharing what experience I had, and helping them find the resources they needed.

The community provides an almost automatic bond. It is like a secret handshake that ensures safety and trust. It was something that opened doors for interviews when I started this book. Even though I was often talking to people I had never met, we were not strangers. We had a bond, a shared experience and understanding that negated the need for the normal formalities between strangers. We were like old friends who had not seen each other for a long time. We had a lot of catching up to do.

Many newly diagnosed patients feel the way I did in the beginning: disconnected and alone. Breast cancer intrudes upon our lives in ways that outsiders cannot understand. It took me years before I could see that being a healthy survivor did not exclude me from the community. That very small lesion in my breast changed my life. It impacted my family and friends. It gave me closer relationships and even insight into myself. It gave me access to stories that continue to inspire me and help me grow.

Kris is the founder of a group called the Firefly Sisterhood in Minnesota. Before starting her nonprofit, Kris found research on the power of one-on-one connections for women going through breast cancer treatment. She embraced the concept and created an organization that uses breast cancer survivors as "guides" for women who are newly diagnosed. The organization makes intentional matches, conducting an extensive interview with each newly diagnosed woman and finding out what her greatest concerns and fears are, what type of breast cancer she has, the stage, and more about her life. Staff then match her with a survivor who shares some similar characteristics and can guide her through her journey. For example, if a single mother's greatest concern is for her children, the ideal guide might be another single mother who went through treatment and can share ideas and resources as well as provide emotional support. A newly diagnosed woman who is at stage 4 might match best with someone who was also diagnosed at stage 4 and is in long-term remission. The matched pair then determine the nature and frequency of their connection. The

Firefly Sisterhood makes the matches, but the type of relationship varies. Some women meet face to face on a regular basis. Others choose to email or text regularly.

Despite the interviews and the careful matching, relationships don't always work well. Sometimes the connection is not there or the match is not the best. Other times the newly diagnosed woman just isn't ready to join the sisterhood. Her whole life has been disrupted, and she may need some time for personal adjustment, just as I did, before she is ready. Sometimes life just gets in the way, and the logistics don't work. However, most women find it helpful to have a friend who understands. Interestingly, the satisfaction with matches is even higher among the guides than it is among the newly diagnosed.[27] Perhaps this relates to the amount of time women have had to process their personal journey, or perhaps it is the satisfaction that comes from helping others that provides closure for the guides.

Diane is a survivor who wanted community around breast cancer and started a Christian organization called the Comfort Club. She wrote:

> I wasn't really looking for a new ministry when I was diagnosed with breast cancer, but I always say that God has used my journey for good. In the summer of 2006, following surgery, and while I was going through chemo, I met with a few other women I knew who were also going through treatment for breast cancer. We shared stories, encouraged one another, prayed for each other, and agreed to meet again. Soon we were more than just a few friends comforting one another; we were dozens of women on the journey. We called ourselves breast friends and thrivers and joked about naming the group Bosomless Buddies or the Young and the Breastless.

---

27 This information came from a 2016 satisfaction survey of Firefly participants and guides.

Diane's inspiration came from 2 Corinthians 1:3–5 (NIV): "Praise be to God and Father of our Lord Jesus Christ, the Father of compassion and the God of all comfort, who comforts us in all our troubles, so that we can comfort those in any trouble with the comfort we ourselves have received from God. For just as the sufferings of Christ flow over into our lives, so also our comfort abounds through Christ."

Whether support comes from a group, an assigned guide, or a friend, it is an important part of healing. All aspects of health—physical, social, environmental, emotional, spiritual, and intellectual—need to be addressed for healing to be complete. Breast cancer touches all six aspects in different ways. During my early breast cancer journey, my health-care team was focused solely on the physical aspect of my disease. I was left to my own devices for the rest. It wasn't until much later that I discovered the community and realized all the benefits it can offer.

Not everyone is ready to join a support group or become part of a community at the time of diagnosis. Many of us start out in survival mode. We are so focused on the diagnosis and the plan that we don't even recognize we need other forms of support.

We all need to find our own markers along our own paths. A diagnosis such as breast cancer is life changing, but it takes time to process the changes and to accept them. It intrudes on every aspect of life. Each person goes through stages of adjustment that are fluid and must be processed and incorporated into a new reality. The disease has a strong emotional impact on those around us as well as on us ourselves. We need to deal with all the combined emotional fallout while simultaneously adjusting to physical changes in our bodies.

Stories are powerful teachers. I realized their impact as my friends and I shared our stories with one another. I saw the healing effect that sharing my own story had on friends who were facing the fear that comes with a new diagnosis. The healing of sharing was reciprocal, and I felt my own strength grow as I provided hope to friends. I began to understand my own journey better.

It is common for those who have survived the initial journey of diagnosis and treatment to want to "give back" in some way. Many join support groups or mentorship programs in order to relate to others who have shared breast cancer experiences. They want to belong to a community that understands and to extend that understanding to others who need their support. Others join efforts to raise money to help others who are struggling financially because of the disease or to donate to breast cancer research.

Those who have gone through the same or similar challenges can understand and offer support in a way that those who have not been there cannot. Sometimes the challenge is finding the right group or support person to meet personal needs. Lisa was a strong proponent of support groups. She was diagnosed at stage 4, which made finding the right group a little bit of a challenge, but she found the benefit well worth the effort.

I would reemphasize the value of a support group. For me, in the end, it has become as much a social connection with the people that understand what you are going through. Even before it gets to that point, I think it is a valuable part of the process. It certainly doesn't hurt anything. It gives you an avenue and a time set aside where you can talk to people who can relate.

A stage 4 diagnosis or a recurrence that has spread is so different from anything else. At one of our support group meetings, one of the women came and initiated a conversation about donating your body to science for cancer research. She had already done the research at the university here, so she explained the process to us. What was probably even more fascinating was the part of the conversation about how, after they use the body, they cremate whatever they have left and return the ashes to the surviving spouse or family member. It was really a fascinating conversation. The conversation lasted twenty or twenty-five minutes, after which I was thinking that not a lot of people spend time having this kind of discussion.

There were two people in this group who had gotten a little friendly, and the one who initiated the discussion passed away first, and the other one was there when she died and was there when they came to pick up the body. She came back to the support group after that and told us how it all went. She [the friend of the woman who died] had also committed to do the same thing. Sadly, a month later she [also] passed away. Apparently there was a run on questions at the U about how this works following our discussion. That's what I was told, anyway. The moral of the story was that you really get to talk about things that everybody should think about, but rarely do people take the time to do that.

There was another person I met at an all-stage breast cancer group who had already metastasized and said that she did not come to the stage 4 group because "you guys are scary." I said, "Come try it; it's not all about death and dying." She is now an integral part of the group.

We survivors are a club that nobody wants to join, but we are an amazing community, a community of fierce, undefeatable warriors. Christian was viewing pictures from the SCAR Project breast cancer photography collection with his wife. He looked at the scars and saw pain. She looked at the faces and saw strength.[28]

28 The SCAR Project: Breast Cancer Is Not a Pink Ribbon, http://www.thescarproject.org.

Chapter 10

MOVING
ON

Race for the Cure 2010.

Here I Sit

Here I sit in my chemo chair—reminiscing about my hair.
As I look around at all the faces,
I realize cancer comes from many places.
It does not discriminate based on short or tall
and doesn't care if you are big or small.
We sit in our chairs minding our own business as the IV drips . . .
drips continuous.
Sometimes the room is full to the brim,
and other times it seems I am the only one in.
As I continue to sit and receive my treatment
I look around with pure amazement.
People are talking and chatting with friends,
you would never know we are all sick and just hoping to mend.
There is a sense of connection where words are unspoken.
We are all fighting a piece inside that has shattered and broken.
Cancer thinks it can take our courage and spirit
but if you ask anyone here they will say "no way—I won't let it."
So as the drip drip of the IV comes to an end, I am grateful for these
strangers who I know deep down are really all God's friends.

—SUSAN PETTIT

RELATIONSHIPS

Life is about relationships. Even before birth, an infant has bonded with their mother, and sometimes with other family members. When my daughter was pregnant with her third child, her five-year-old son was eye to eye with her belly and talked to the baby on a regular basis. The first time he spoke to his sister after she was born, it was obvious that she recognized his voice. The bond they created while she was in utero had endured.

True human relationship means shared fear and pain. Another person's fear becomes our fear, and their pain becomes our pain. Breast cancer is not a solitary experience, though it may seem lonely at times. We bring others along on our journey. No matter how hard we try to protect them from the pain we are experiencing, they are part of it.

Dick was the primary caregiver for his wife, Maren, and blogged about his experience. This particular entry illustrates the toll breast cancer treatment can take:

> Here's a fun one for you to try sometime. Don't shave for a couple of days, throw on a dirty hunting coat and some ski wax–encrusted Crocs, then stand around looking really fidgety and impatient and vaguely deranged while the nice ladies at Target fill a Percocet prescription. The DEA agents should be pulling up in our driveway shortly.

One word, *cancer,* and your life and the lives of those around you change forever. One of the difficulties with a potentially life-threatening diagnosis is that family dynamics often place the patient in the paradoxical position of both providing and receiving care. This is particularly true of breast cancer, which is prevalent in women, particularly middle-aged women, who are often the major source of care and support for both younger and older family members. Many of us find ourselves reassuring family and worrying about how they are taking our diagnosis at the very time when we ourselves are in our greatest hour of emotional need. We try to balance self-care and care for others. Too often, we prioritize care for others at the expense of self-care. Our bond with loved ones is so strong that we nurture instinctively.

We need to recognize that we cannot continue to care for them if we don't care for ourselves. We need to let ourselves be cared for during treatment and even afterwards while we are healing and adjusting to life after cancer.

During treatment, family, friends, and coworkers understand that you need care. Some know exactly what to do. They volunteer for the small tasks that may seem overwhelming. They find ways to provide cheer. For the person who is used to being the caregiver, it may be hard to let others take over. While they may be thankful for the help, they may feel inadequate when they are unable to do things for themselves and their loved ones. My students were wonderful while I was going through treatment; various ones often stopped by my office to see how I was feeling, sometimes bringing small gifts such as tea or coffee.

In the words of one of my interviewees, "Breast cancer really shows you who your true friends are." The friends who help us step away for a moment and make us laugh or who can anticipate our needs make the journey a little easier. They provide a ray of sunshine, an opportunity to forget cancer and feel human for a little while. The friends who cannot understand what we are going through or who cannot face their own fears often become distant.

Other people don't know what to say or how to act. They may stand by in discomfort or even seem to disappear. Some people are there for you during your journey, and some friends just don't get it.

Dick described it well when he said, "There are people who—you tell them about a diagnosis of breast cancer, and they are completely blown apart, and then there are some that are like, 'Oh, yeah, that is kind of like the flu.'" He said he learned to tailor his conversations with friends to their ability to understand and respond.

Self-care is an important part of healing and of moving on. After radiation, I was tired. I wanted to keep up with my breakneck schedule but found I often needed to take a short nap when I got home. Getting started in the morning was equally hard; I often found myself standing in the shower, still soaking wet, searching for the energy to get out and dry myself off. I knew that I needed to exercise to regain my strength and start to feel vibrant again, but finding the energy was hard. The dog wanted a walk at the end of the day, and I knew we both needed that walk, but it was hard to find the energy. If he hadn't been so insistent, we might not have done it, but getting out in the fresh air and walking was the best thing for me.

It took longer to get back into other types of exercise. My arm muscles had weakened from inactivity during radiation. My balance was not very good. I didn't have the energy to push myself too hard. I had to adjust to the changes in my body.

There were other adjustments as well. Cancer forces introspection. It changes perspectives and priorities. It changes relationships. Life is not the same as it was before. We are not the same as we were before cancer. Neither are our families.

FINDING MEANING

Survivor guilt is loosely defined as guilt one feels when one survives something that someone else did not. It often comes with the question of why: "Why did I survive when someone else did not?" I experienced survivor guilt. Six weeks after my double mastectomy I was in Nicaragua, where most people do not have access to breast cancer screening. By the time their cancer is diagnosed, it is usually advanced and hard to treat, and often they don't have access to treatment at all. It all seemed so unfair. Why did I have the right to prompt and comprehensive treatment when they did not? Why was I privileged while they were not? While my Nicaraguan friends were happy that I was well, I felt embarrassed—not by my cancer but by my privilege.

My survivor guilt was like a trap. It held me down. It kept me from moving forward. It made it hard for me to relate to other people who had cancer, at least at first. I felt like an impostor. Yes, I had been diagnosed with cancer, but mine had been so minor an experience compared to theirs. I had not suffered the way so many had.

I tried to make myself part of the community of breast cancer patients and survivors. I did the Susan G. Komen Race for the Cure and the 3-Day breast cancer walk. In both events I was surrounded by other people who had experienced breast cancer and by their families. Despite the camaraderie around me, I was alone. I didn't speak to anyone for the first two days of the three-day walk. Finally, I found a former student of mine who was walking for a friend who was too sick to walk. She and her friends welcomed me to their group and made me feel supported.

It took time for me to heal emotionally and to realize that each journey is different. We each have to process our own experience and make sense out of it in our own way. We all have to move on to a new life when we are ready.

I have heard survivors say that they look at life differently now. They have a new perspective that helps them separate what is important from what is not. They find joy in small things that they paid little attention to before.

Others become frustrated. They feel that their old life no longer fits. Old friends and even some family members don't understand how they have changed. This can be difficult to deal with. Relationships can bend to the breaking point. The fear of recurrence can lead to anxiety or depression. The fatigue and other residual effects of cancer treatment can make it difficult to function and can add to frustration and depression.

GIVING BACK

Healing, both physical and emotional, takes time. It makes us slow down and gives us time for reflection, introspection, and perspective.

A new perspective on life often includes a desire to give back, to help others along the way, just as the survivor was helped by so many as they adjusted to their diagnosis and went through treatment. Often they found strength in the community of breast cancer survivors and want to provide that kind of support to others.

Giving back brings as much joy to the giver as to the recipient—or more. This phenomenon can be life changing. It is the oxymoron of breast cancer: that the worst thing that happens in life can also be the best thing.

Part 3

TRANSFORMATIONS:
FINDING PURPOSE

The True Miracle

Inside the Miracle
eye of the storm
a stillness
flashing true understanding
of purpose not cause

We never resolve the mystery of
Cancer's intrusion nor
what helped cure the physical disease

but the true Miracle
is not cure
but what is healed
the spark ignited
that fires future with promise

—MORRY EDWARDS

Chapter 11

BOTH SIDES
NOW

The author posing by a Dr. McDreamy image.

From "**How Do You Feel**"

How do I feel?
I don't know how I feel about MY cancer!
Part of my femininity has been cut off.
Dissected and trashed like garbage.
I've been wounded.
How do I feel?
I've been cheated.
This wasn't supposed to happen to me.
I've been a good girl,
a poster child for healthy living.
No illness was supposed to attack me.

I've gotten to know cancer (from arm's length)
As the therapist who
guides OTHER people with this illness.
I expected immunity
in exchange for my work
It was a bargain with life
I thought I had made.

—GAY WALKER

PROVIDER TO PATIENT AND BACK AGAIN

My diagnostic process was pretty routine the first time around.
I wasn't surprised when I received the call to come back
for a second mammogram—I'd been through that before.
I had a history of fibrocystic disease, which sometimes made
mammograms hard to read. I put it off. I was busy. After a
while, it slipped my mind.

I still wasn't surprised when my doctor called me herself. She
was very thorough. Besides, she was a friend. She followed up on
everything. I made the appointment for the mammogram to make
her happy. I still wasn't worried.

After performing the mammogram, the tech asked me to wait
while the radiologist reviewed the films. She came back and did
a few additional views, again asking me to wait. This time the
radiologist came back with her. I needed a biopsy, he told me, then
apologized that he didn't have a same-day appointment to do it but
scheduled me for the next day.

I've sent many patients for mammograms and biopsies. I
knew the routine. I still wasn't worried. I wasn't even running
the statistics through my head. I hardly noticed the tiny twinge
of unease at the pit of my stomach as I picked up one of the free
emery boards from the lobby on my way out.

The next day I put on one of the nice robes provided by
the breast center and sat down on the procedure table. My
appointment started with small talk while the radiologist and
the ultrasound tech prepared for my procedure. They laid out
their instruments while we talked about the weather. Then the
radiologist explained what he was going to do. My interest at that
point was more academic than personal. I had referred women for
this procedure, but I really had very little idea exactly how it was
done or what to expect.

The needle was less painful than I had anticipated. Once it was inserted, I shifted my attention to the ultrasound screen. I have always been a watcher, maybe because of what I do. I had watched when I'd had my finger stitched up after a scalpel blade slipped when I was a student. I've watched my colonoscopies to make sure no polyps were missed. I watch when my blood is drawn. So of course I was watching the screen during my biopsy. We were looking for two lumps that had been identified on mammogram. First, a small, round lesion appeared on the screen. I watched as the needle approached it. The lesion disappeared as soon as the needle hit it. Good—it was a cyst. The mood in the room became cautiously festive. After a few minutes of searching, the other lump came into view. It was different. It was not round and smooth. I knew what it was immediately: it was cancer. It was a spiculated mass, with all of the characteristics I describe to students when I teach about breast cancer.

I had barely let the idea of cancer enter my mind prior to my biopsy, but I was not surprised when I saw the cancer on the ultrasound screen, and I was not surprised when I received the phone call the next day.

I wasn't surprised, but suddenly I was face to face with my own mortality. The realization that I could die was completely physical. I was no longer the watcher. The academic curiosity was replaced in one instant by an unfamiliar feeling in the pit of my stomach: fear. Fear numbed my intelligence and made it hard to function in the moment. That was the moment when I transitioned from a health-care provider to a cancer patient.

I was beginning a long journey toward understanding. Each experience in our lives changes us. The changes may be barely noticeable or they may be transformative. For me, it often takes years to process change. I try to reject it, pretend it has no effect on me, but it does. I need time to recognize the change, adjust to it, and even embrace it as an integral part of myself. Now, more than ever before, when I am delivering bad news to a patient I am feeling some of their pain. The pit of my stomach clenches in sympathy.

Health-care providers who are also survivors often face the challenge of playing two roles simultaneously. We are both patient and caregiver. This was particularly difficult for my friend Carol Ann, who had just started a new job at a cancer center four months prior to her breast cancer diagnosis. She had a difficult work and insurance situation that highlights some of the unique struggles people in the medical field face when they become patients. Her insurance covered her care within the system where she worked but would not cover all her care if she went elsewhere. She felt vulnerable. She wanted to create separation between work and what was going on personally, but that option didn't exist. Work and personal life were all happening in the same space. She did not have the luxury of time to process and adjust. She had to deal with her own diagnosis while simultaneously caring for patients and adjusting to her role in a new team.

The other complication she faced was that the person who had held her position previously had died of cancer, and her new team was still reeling from that experience. She, as their new manager, had to be part of their healing even when she herself was in need of their support. It was a difficult dance. This is how she described it:

> Knowing what I knew, there was no way in the world I was going to reach for my team. So there was this incredible dichotomy: I can see these services, I know they're available, I'm a proponent of them, I'm a practitioner, and I cannot reach within the cancer center. So I had to reach elsewhere. I had

to reach to colleagues outside for emotional support. I had to reach outside of the patient support and education team. Fortunately, that circle of support was there, and people responded to my request for support. I was and am grateful for that. I know, I knew and I know, how helpful it is to have that additional emotional support. So many challenges . . .

I actually didn't spend a lot of time considering myself because of where I worked. I had to put my manager hat on and show up as the manager of a cancer center day after day after day. I had to have consideration for my team. It was more than taking care of myself. It was really being mindful of many others.

While Carol Ann's circumstances were unique, her story has much in common with those of other providers who are also patients or survivors. We are in the unique position of having empathy based on experience but needing to observe professional boundaries with both patients and coworkers. We also need to be aware that our experiences are colored by our knowledge, our training, and our professional roles and may be vastly different from the experiences of others.

My second breast cancer diagnosis highlighted the question of professional boundaries in a different way. I am both a medical provider and a teacher. Our physician assistant program has a cohort of thirty-two students each year in an integrated curriculum that requires faculty and students to work very closely together. We get to know each other very well.

When I found a small lump just above my left implant, I was surprised. I knew that my chances of recurrence were slight, but I also knew that I needed to have the lump evaluated. The first thing I did was talk to one of my teaching colleagues who worked in oncology. She was not part of my care team but served as a second opinion when discussing options. She encouraged me to have it evaluated and walked me through what that might entail.

I started with my primary physician. When I arrived at my appointment, the nurse informed me that my doctor had a student and asked whether I was okay with the student being present for my exam. Being a medical educator, I gave consent without hesitation. The nurse returned to inform me that the student was one of mine and asked me again whether that was okay. I hesitated briefly at the thought of showing my breasts to a student I knew well but decided it was a unique teaching moment and consented. After the exam, I invited the student to attend my biopsy, giving her an additional opportunity to learn. It actually made the process easier, as I was able to concentrate on her learning rather than my own apprehension.

The biopsy results were positive: I had breast cancer again. I scheduled an appointment with the surgeon, only to have the process of giving consent for student involvement repeated. My surgeon was also a clinical preceptor who was accompanied by yet another of my students. It was a difficult visit. I could see in the student's eyes how difficult it was for her to be part of the discussion of a new cancer diagnosis, but I also recognized how valuable the experience was for her education, even more valuable that she was facing this with someone she knew.

Having two students involved in my care caused another dilemma. I knew that the whole situation was difficult for them. They were emotionally involved but bound by rules of confidentiality, so reaching out for support from classmates, friends, or family members was not an option. This prompted my decision to make my diagnosis public even though I might have preferred to keep it private, at least for a little longer, so that I could adjust myself before dealing with the reaction of others. Out of respect for them, I shared my diagnosis with students and colleagues, giving the two who were involved in my care permission to talk about any struggles they were having.

In my clinical practice, I could be more selective about revealing my diagnosis. I chose to tell the scheduler and my supervisor so that I could reduce my clinic schedule if needed, but I did not feel the need to let any of my clinical colleagues know my personal history or my new diagnosis. I could continue per usual.

FINDING MY OWN IDENTITY AS A SURVIVOR

My own experience with breast cancer is like a key that has opened additional doors. It has given me the secret handshake that lets other survivors know that I am part of the community and that it is safe to share their story with me. Their stories have made me realize how little I know, even with all my training and experience, and how little they know about the condition that changes lives forever. As Carol Ann explained:

> We had our first cancer survivor celebration the last Saturday in June, just a couple of weeks ago, and Ruth Bachman was the keynote speaker. She uses an hourglass as her prop and turns it. The sand is the same sand but in a different form, a different arrangement. I think that is so telling. I know that to others I look and seem the same, but I know that internally there is a lot that has been rearranged. It is not always easy to articulate and not always appropriate to articulate.

As I have mentioned, many of the breast cancer events I attended early on did not feel like a fit for me. I didn't feel connected. By contrast, I feel an immediate connection with other survivors when we are one on one, whether it is in the clinical setting or in the broader community. I understand that the other side of the hourglass is different. I also understand that we each have a unique experience that transforms our lives in a way that, while it may have some commonalities, is not the same for everyone. I recognize the need for community, if not in the form of a group then in conversation with someone who understands, who can help us answer our questions, and can relate to feelings that may be hard to express to others.

It is not in my character to start a foundation or join a large group for fundraising. It is, however, very comfortable for me to share information, to listen, and to teach.

EMPATHY AND COMMUNICATION

I have learned a lot about breast cancer since my own diagnosis. It has made me more observant of the challenges faced by patients and more cognizant of the impact those challenges have on every aspect of life. I have had the honor and the privilege of being let into very intimate parts of my patients' lives. Their stories have helped grow my compassion and my understanding.

Our life experiences make us better medical providers. We can relate better if we have had experiences similar to those of the people we are treating. Experience grows our compassion. Since my second diagnosis, I have joked that this time around I am doing field research. My first personal experience with breast cancer taught me a lot, but I needed to know more. This time my treatment was more complicated and extensive. I experienced some of the adverse effects that I had only heard about before.

I also got to know the oncology team better and came to appreciate the importance of their compassion and attention to detail.

Compassion is an integral part of medical care. It can be a frightening concept for new providers—we fear that if we are too compassionate, we will feel too much pain, that it will interfere with our ability to be objective in our care. We fear that our supply of compassion is limited and that we will eventually run out of it and become jaded and cold. This is not true. Compassion grows compassion. I recently read an article that asked, "Does taking time for compassion make doctors better at their jobs?" It concluded that research showed there was less burnout among physicians who took time for compassion.

In my own practice, I have noticed that my most satisfying shifts are those when I am able to sit down with someone who is suffering or scared and listen to their concerns. I cannot always solve their problems, but listening with compassion has a healing effect.

We learn compassion through experience. Parenting teaches us to appreciate the joys and challenges faced by parents. Experiencing pain, fear, and disease makes us attuned to the suffering of others.

We also learn by modeling the actions and attitudes of others. My care team has been wonderful. Each and every person, from the receptionists to the radiation technicians to the oncologists, has been an important teacher. I want to emulate them in my own practice and make my own patients feel as cared for as I felt under their care.

Patients are perhaps our best teachers. When we show even the slightest compassion, they let us into intimate corners of their lives, places where no one else has gone. Their stories show us aspects of life that we have not experienced ourselves. We need to honor their experiences and accept them as valuable gifts. Their experiences are our teachers. If we can connect with their stories, we can grow our wisdom and compassion. We can then pass on what we learned to others by providing compassionate care.

Compassion is not a sad thing. It is not always tears and hugs. Compassion can be an opportunity to laugh or a distraction, such as looking for Waldo on the ceiling of the radiation room. It can be a small thing, such as a nice robe for treatment or a bowl of candy at the reception desk.

Chapter 12

BEYOND BORDERS: TARA'S STORY

Tara with a Tanzanian colleague and student.

We Remember Them

After a poem by Rabbi Sylvan Kamens
and Rabbi Jack Riemer

As our alarm greets us before dawn making a call to rise;
We remember them.
As we don our scrubs in the dim light of the morning
so as not to wake our loved ones;
We remember them.
As we sip our coffee and prepare to face what the new day brings;
We remember them.
As we drive through traffic away from
the comforts of home and family;
We remember them.
As the noise and bustle of the hospital fill our ears;
We remember them.
As we walk by colleagues already busy at work on the floor;
We remember them.
As long as we practice, we will sacrifice for those we care for as,
We remember them.
When our hearts are struck with grief as we deliver unwelcome news;
We remember them.
When we feel we can no longer move forward past our tears;
We remember them.
When we are forced to make decisions for those who cannot speak;
We remember them.
When we see the smiles in the eyes of those we have helped;
We remember them.
When we return home and try to quiet our busy minds;
We remember them.
For as long as we can work, their memories will live with us,
for they are now a part of us as,
We remember them.

—BESS KUZMA

WORK STRESS MANAGEMENT

Patients and their families are not the only ones whose lives are changed by breast cancer. The medical staff members who take care of them cannot help but be impacted by the patients they care for. The stories of their patients intertwine with their own. They rejoice at the good news and cry when things do not go well. They recognize that even the smallest thing they do can be helpful while at the same time yearning to be able to do more.

Tara is a physician assistant (PA) who has been working in oncology since graduating from PA school. Oncology is an unusual first position for a young PA; most people see it as a sad, depressing atmosphere and can't imagine working in such an environment day after day. Tara saw it as a way to ease the pain of others, a way to alleviate fear. She found that taking an interest in her patients and listening carefully to their stories helped them through even the most painful procedures.

When asked about managing the sadness and pain of cancer and cancer-related deaths, Tara explained that death is a part of life. It is inevitable that if someone is born, they will die. Birth is a time of celebration. Tara feels that death should be equally honored. She feels that her job is to make the passing as comfortable and honored as possible while preventing death and helping to improve quality of life for survivors when possible.

That doesn't mean that cancer and death are easy to deal with on a daily basis. Tara rides her bicycle to and from work each day as a way to find solitude and time to process the events of the day so as not to carry them home with her.

Caring for cancer patients in a major teaching hospital is a tough job. The patients there are often the sickest and the most difficult to treat. Delivering state-of-the-art, cutting-edge care to very sick patients requires exceptional skill, and treatment is often long and difficult. Patients and their care teams get to know one another better than might be the case in a less academic setting. One of Tara's patients had a passion for matchmaking and attempted to connect Tara with a young resident from Argentina who was also on her care team. Despite the patient's persistence, Tara resisted. She felt it would be highly unprofessional to go along with her patient's matchmaking attempts. The patient did not survive, but her efforts apparently had some effect: shortly after the patient's death, the young resident she had targeted asked Tara out, and Tara said yes. On their first date, they happened to run into the patient's husband. That was an omen. Tara and José, now a physician and cancer researcher, are married and working together to improve cancer care around the world.

FINDING PURPOSE IN AFRICA

Over the past few years, through colleagues at work, Tara has been involved with the Foundation for Cancer Care in Tanzania. The organization recently built a new cancer center in northern Tanzania that provides services such as radiation and chemotherapy treatments, which are practically nonexistent in that country. Through this organization and their research, Tara and José have traveled to Tanzania multiple times.

Besides serving on the board of the foundation, Tara has found other ways to expand cancer care in Tanzania. She has obtained grants to fund efforts that have raised awareness and recognition of early signs of cancer and has started a cervical cancer screening program as well as conducted workshops to teach breast cancer screening techniques. As an adjunct professor in a PA program, she has taken students with her, helping to create a new generation of globally concerned and active medical providers in both the United States and Tanzania. She has also arranged for learning and teaching opportunities in the United States for a Tanzanian colleague.

Tara's compassion toward her patients has grown into a larger mission that is radiating across the globe. She is constantly striving to increase the impact of her work through networking, education, and research. She recognizes that one person can make only a small impact on cancer care for individual patients but that many joined together can make a much bigger and longer-lasting impact on many. Besides her work in Tanzania and her research on cancer treatment throughout Africa, Tara's teaching and networking efforts continue to inspire a future generation of providers and researchers on several continents.

We hope and pray that someday cancer will no longer be the devastating disease that we know today, but for the present, all we can do is support one another and try to do what little we can. Life experiences promote growth, even when the seed is something as painful as cancer. Tara has been watering seeds and helping patients and students grow by focusing on the person in front of her. Her patients and students have inspired her to broaden her perspective and, through research and global work, to look beyond the individual patient and to make a difference in the world.

Chapter 13

MAKING A DIFFERENCE AT HOME:

HALIMA'S STORY

Women at a cancer screening clinic in Tanzania.

From "**Electric Lady**"

*Electric Lady, you know it's you
and what it is that you must do
with what lies buried deep inside of you.
So please, Electric Lady, don't be blue.*

*You shine so bright from inner light.
It's darkness that you fear.
Stop anger and hate; let Love radiate
with each unfolding year.*

*It's time to change—you know it's true.
Bring out the child who's locked in you.
Though it can hurt to feel so much,
the world needs your perceptive touch.*

—JULIETTA CHEVALIER

FROM SICKNESS TO HEALTH AND BACK

Halima's story is one of unparalleled success. She grew up on a farm in the Kilimanjaro Region of northern Tanzania, the youngest child in a large family. Her mother had nine children; her father was polygamous, with two wives and seventeen children all together. Halima worked hard and did well in school. Her father encouraged his children to go as far as their capacity would take them, and Halima had plenty of capacity. She earned a bachelor's degree in social work and graduated with honors. She worked as a librarian for two years before going back to school for a master's degree in information science. By the time she finished that degree she was married and had one child, but she wasn't finished with her education. She left her son at home and went to study in the United Kingdom. There, she finished a master's in education while her husband was finishing his PhD there.

Over time, Halima became interested in gender issues in Tanzania. She took a job as a gender activist in a trade union, where she was the director for women and youth. Much of her work centered around sexual harassment, gender discrimination, equal opportunities, and educating women about labor laws.

After ten years, she was appointed the governor of her district in northern Tanzania, and two years later she was promoted to governor at the provincial level. Her life and her success story are an inspiration to young girls.

The first thing Halima noticed that clued her to a health problem was fatigue. She tried to ignore it, but it continued, and after four years she decided to have a medical evaluation. The fatigue seemed excessive even for a hardworking woman balancing family and a demanding career. The results of her evaluation were uncertain. She was told, "Mama, maybe you have a problem with your heart. Maybe you have this . . ." But it was "maybe."

After ten years of vague symptoms and many medical visits that failed to diagnose her problem, she was feeling very weak. A nurse at a women's medical association found two lumps in Halima's breast. The organization, one that Halima had worked with in the past, did a lot of breast cancer screening, which was uncommon in Tanzania at that time. Halima was shocked. She had been told that her symptoms were due to an enlarged heart.

After more evaluations at larger, better-equipped hospitals, Halima's diagnosis was confirmed—she had breast cancer. That's when her nightmare began. She explained:

So I started looking for how to get the treatment. That was my major headache because in Tanzania once you are diagnosed with cancer, really it is a death sentence. I talked to the doctor and I said, "What should I do?" The doctor recommended a mastectomy, the only treatment available locally.

The other option Halima was given was a referral to India for treatment:

I said, "India? Is there no other place?" They said, "No, India because India is cheap." That was the only place they wanted to refer me. I said, "How good are they?" He said about 50 percent.

With her life hanging in the balance, Halima had to find a solution quickly. She called a doctor who had been her friend for years, and the friend encouraged her to try to go to America for treatment. This seemed like an impossible recommendation until a different friend reminded her of several American doctors she had befriended and helped when they had been in Tanzania. This friend contacted the American doctors and asked for their help.

They remembered me. They said, "Tell her not to go anywhere else, but to come here."

My doctor told them that it was very expensive to go there and the government wanted to send me to India. They said to tell them to just give me the airline ticket and not to worry about anything else. They said they were going to see the president of their hospital. So that's how my journey started. Just like angels coming from heaven.

The next step was harder. Halima had to go to the Prime Minister and ask for a ticket to the United States instead of the referral to India. She was asked when she would be back and what she planned to do about her job. Finally, she was able to secure the plane ticket but nothing else, including no funds for treatment or expenses. She was flying on faith. She and her husband sold their car and took off for the United States.

Halima's cancer was already at stage four when she finally started treatment. The separation from her children was hard. Halima had not told them she had cancer prior to leaving Tanzania. She hadn't wanted them to worry. After months of separation and treatments, her MRIs were clear. She finally heard the words she had been waiting for:

"You can go home. You can come back after a year or six months if you are able to get a ticket, and we will check you again."

I went back home. Now when I went back home, they had given my job to somebody else because I had cancer. They didn't expect me to go back alive.

Halima received six months of continued hormone therapy, after which her scans were still clear. Halima didn't believe the doctors at first. She asked for more radiation or some other treatment.

Halima knows that she was extremely lucky. She knows that her life was saved by her position of privilege and personal connections. Through her work as a women's advocate, she is acutely aware that most women in Tanzania do not have the same opportunities.

MAKING A DIFFERENCE AT HOME

Breast cancer is a particularly devastating disease in Tanzania. As Halima started talking to other women with breast cancer, they found support in one another. She described their situation:

> Once you are diagnosed with cancer people just think you are going to die, so there is a big problem of stigma. When we are hearing testimonies from the women, we find that many of the men throw them away and marry other women or have a woman on the side. The stigma associated with cancer is because it is a disease that is long term. It is a long journey that has no end or beginning. The end is when you die. You are always waiting for a recurrence and things like that. It is also about telling the family that it is okay because the wounds are often very deep. For the survivor it is now impossible for marriage. Women will shy away from that. They are not sexually active also. It is a big blow to the happiness of most of the women. It is also the hygienic conditions, the poor diet, women having many, many children. If she has no provider, where will she go? The woman is working, but she is working in [her husband's] land to provide for her children. So those are the kinds of stigma that are very bad. It is like when people

started talking about HIV/AIDS. What if someone doesn't even have breasts? It is their dignity. Your dignity is gone.

I think as our group grows these women can come together, and if we can build skill [they can] survive on their own and maybe even have a source for a loan. Maybe we can provide small loans for women to start up a business. We have good ideas about how we are going to help. Our aim is to be able to partner with other organizations.

Halima visits women in the hospital who have undergone mastectomy and sees the shame that they feel due to the disfigurement and how it devastates their self-esteem. She has collected breast prostheses and breast cancer bras from contacts in the United States to help the women she visits. She now has a project for women with breast cancer that includes a place for the women to stay near the hospital while they are receiving treatment, as well as sewing machines to help them to support themselves. She also does breast cancer advocacy programs on TV and has been a featured speaker for the Foundation for Cancer Care in Tanzania to help the organization raise money for a new cancer center that recently opened in the northern part of the country.

Halima is no longer the governor of her province, but she is still a powerful force advocating for women and working for changes that will save lives. She wants to take away the stigma surrounding breast cancer, to remove the death sentence, and to help women find meaningful life after cancer.

Unfortunately, like that of so many other survivors, Halima's remission has ended. With her own health issues, it is hard to continue. The hope for the women she works with lies in medical improvements and better understanding of breast cancer through the work of the Foundation for Cancer Care in Tanzania and other organizations. With increased treatment options and longer survival, breast cancer may be seen as less threatening. Stigma may decrease as more women survive and are able to care for themselves and their families and to tell their stories. The new cancer center in northern Tanzania is bringing hope to many with this disease. The word *cancer* may no longer be synonymous with death.

Chapter 14

QUILTS AND COMMUNICATION: ANITA'S STORY

the story of
Deaf breast cancer
survivors,
their families
and the
Deaf community.

a documentary film

signing on

May 9, 2015 @ 10:00 a.m.   Admission: $5.00

Sponsored by: Riverview Theater
The Pink Deafies   3800 42nd Ave
CONTACT: anita@deafchw.org   Mpls MN 55406

Poster for Anita's documentary film.

From "**Prayer for the Ministering Women**"

The quiltmaker brings her pieces of colored cloth, tosses them into the air,
and catches them in the most beautiful arrangement.
Another can grab pictures out of the thin air and show us to ourselves. . . .
Mother Father God, you have given us our talents,
and we offer them back to you as gifts.
Our medicines, steaming towels, bubble baths, chicken stock, jokes,
flowers, music, and our full hearts.
Medicine woman God, we ask that your healing power
flow through our hands to Mary.
Let our touch be your touch. Infuse her medicines with your grace.
Healer of our memories, you see into our hearts.
Please mend the hurtful parts of our past.
Remove the scars that block the flow of your healing energy.
Author of time, your time is not our time.
You have placed infinity in every second, a universe in every cell.
Give Mary all the time she needs to finish her earthly tasks.
You who orders the planets in space, order Mary's cells to your will.

—MARY LANDERS DECKER

THE VOICE IN THE VOID

Anita knew almost nothing about breast cancer when she was diagnosed back in the 1980s. General knowledge about cancer was much less than it is now. Besides that, Anita is Deaf. Knowledge about breast cancer, she learned, was rare in the Deaf community. With the help of a sign-language interpreter, Anita told me about her experience with breast cancer:

> 1983 was my first diagnosis, but two years before that I actually had found the lump, and so I had been going to get it checked, and I had been told, "You're too young to have cancer." So of course nothing was investigated. Then I went to a movie at the Deaf club that we have here in town, and there was a Deaf woman who had been diagnosed with breast cancer and was dealing with treatment. She actually had had a full mastectomy. That was the first time I had ever met anybody who had had a mastectomy. I sat down with her and was talking with her about my situation and my lump, and she said, "Get yourself to the doctor and go have a mammogram right now!" I said, "What's a mammogram?" I had never heard of one. I only knew that I had a lump, but I had never had a mammogram. So I did, and I had to fight to get that, even, to get the permission for the test. I wanted a mammogram right then, and they said, "Okay, three months from now we've got an opening."

Even though Anita had found the lump two years before, the doctors thought she was too young to have cancer and did not see any urgency to get a mammogram done. Anita insisted on an expedited mammogram. The findings were a shock:

Of course, they found that I did have breast cancer. I had lymph nodes involved by that time, so the surgery was sixteen lymph nodes out and then ten had already become involved. I had a single mastectomy, chemo . . . yuck, it was awful. Think about it—this was '83, and I was in a tiny little cell, basically, with no communication with anyone in my case. Everybody's around me in a mask. I can't read anybody's lips. I can't do anything. I just felt like I was completely isolated. It was scary. You know what it was like—cancer was basically a death sentence at the time. Certainly, I knew that the word *cancer* meant you were going to die.

At the time, I was young. I had two small children. But I did have a wonderful surgeon, and I said, "I have to survive." The surgeon said, "Do you want to see your kids graduate from high school?" I said yes, and he said, "Fine—we'll do that." It was just that that helped me get through it.

Anita had surgery, chemo, and radiation therapy. A few years later, during her reconstruction process, another lump was discovered and removed. There were no survivorship programs back then, so Anita went about her life. One of the major problems she faced was lack of communication. Not being able to communicate with her caregivers during the diagnostic process had created a very frightening experience for her. She could only see eyes above masks. She couldn't hear what people were saying, and she couldn't even try to read lips because of the masks. Communication continued to be a problem as she tried to process her experience and her fears. She tried a support group but didn't find it helpful. Her inability to communicate made it difficult to get full benefit from the group:

I had a support group that I attended, but at the time, the interpreters we had were not particularly aware or savvy about this process. We were using community interpreters who were not necessarily qualified, or they were trying to find volunteers. All that made things really hard for me, and I noticed people disappearing from the support group. I asked, "Why are people leaving the support group?" I was told, "Oh, that's because they died." I had no idea people weren't coming because they had passed away. This is the kind of information that I wasn't getting.

I remember the number-one discussion in the group was about people's husbands leaving them. I just remember that being part of that whole conversation, and it freaked me out. I would just go home and hug my husband so much and say, "Thank you so much for staying with me." So after a while it became just more negative than positive. I wasn't feeling a strong connection with people and what they were going through. The communication was one way. Because I was sitting there watching an interpreter, my ability to tell my own story was pretty limited.

Anita tried to talk to other Deaf women about breast cancer in order to form their own support group, but she had difficulty finding anyone who would participate. Nobody wanted to talk about it. Breast cancer was a topic surrounded by secrecy, and there was a huge stigma around it in the Deaf community. Anita was told to go home and pay attention to her husband and children as if talking about breast cancer made her a negligent wife and mother. Anita persisted.

BUILDING COMMUNITY

Eventually Anita was able to find a sewing group that had breast cancer survivors among its members. They started with casual conversation about breast cancer, then one thing led to another. Anita became involved in community awareness activities through a group called Pink Deafies and eventually received funding to make a documentary about breast cancer in the Deaf community. She has continued to work as a community health worker raising breast cancer awareness.

Meanwhile, her own cancer journey has also continued. In 2008, her daughter was diagnosed with breast cancer. Anita happened to be receiving an award from Angel Foundation at the time and mentioned her daughter's diagnosis. An oncologist in the audience urged her to make an appointment. Both Anita and her daughter had genetic testing done and were found to be positive for BRCA mutation. Anita had what was supposed to be a prophylactic hysterectomy, but in the process doctors discovered a tiny cancerous cell on her fallopian tube.

In 2013, after the birth of a baby girl, Anita's daughter also had a hysterectomy. When Anita got home from caring for her daughter, she saw her oncologist and again was found to have more tumors, this time just touching her colon.

Anita's cancer journey has spanned more than thirty years and has taught her a lot. She uses what she has learned to help her Deaf community understand cancer and to remove the stigma surrounding it.

ADVICE FOR PROVIDERS

Anita gave me this advice for providers:

> I think what we need is for providers to be more sensitive
> when communicating with us, members of the Deaf
> community. If they're asking about family history for the
> Deaf community, I will guarantee you that 55 percent of
> us do not have any idea what our family history is because
> we don't communicate with our families. They don't know
> our language. Providers need to understand that we can't
> necessarily give accurate information because we don't
> know. I work, of course, as a community health worker, so
> I spend a lot of time now working with providers. Providers
> tend to love to use percentages. They say, "The percent of
> the general population . . ." and we don't understand the
> process because we've not been exposed to much [medical]
> information. We don't understand what a biopsy is. We
> don't know what's going on, what's going to happen next. So
> I spend a lot of time saying, "I don't care about the general
> population, nor does she. For her situation, what will she
> need to go through? What's the next step?"

Anita went on to talk about communication during procedures.
She used a core biopsy as an example. Imagine lying on a table
with the doctor on one side and the interpreter in another part
of the room. If the doctor tries to explain the procedure while
they are doing it, a Deaf patient can see their lips moving but
must watch the interpreter in order to understand what is being
said. This causes the patient to move on the table to try to position
themselves to see the interpreter and may make the biopsy more
difficult. Anita recommends waiting until after the procedure to
talk about it and to ask and answer questions.

She uses her own experiences and the lessons she has learned to help patients navigate medical appointments and understand medical information that may be very difficult for them. As a community health worker, she often becomes a cultural broker, helping bridge the gap between her patients' Deaf culture and the medical community. Her documentary, *Signing On*, has become a valuable tool for medical providers to learn more about the Deaf community and its unique culture.

A recent PA student research project surveyed sign-language interpreters about their perceptions of effective communication. The experience of the interpreters corresponded with Anita's: they felt that Deaf patients often left appointments with a lack of clarity about what was wrong with them or what they needed to do. Sign language is not the same as spoken language. This means that an interpreter is translating a foreign language, which is why written notes are ineffective for communication with the Deaf community. Even with a sign-language interpreter, there is a cultural gap that needs bridging. This often puts the interpreter in the position of translating both language and culture. In addition, health literacy is often low in the Deaf population. Like Anita, many Deaf patients have rudimentary understanding of disease and health care. Providers need to be aware of this. They need to provide extensive patient education and use communication methods that optimize interpretation and ensure understanding.[29]

---

29 Hommes RE, Borash AI, Hartwig K, DeGracia D. "American Sign Language Interpreters Perceptions of Barriers to Healthcare Communication in Deaf and Hard of Hearing Patients," *Journal of Community Health* 43, no. 5 (October 2018): 956–961, https://doi.org/10.1007/s10900-018-0511-3.

Chapter 15

FROM CHEERING ONE TO CHEERING MANY: BOB AND LINDA'S STORY

The author's daughter and a shark at the Mall of America Race for the Cure.

From "**A Sparrow's Tenor**"

It was an April Sunday
I loved seeing you walk through that door.
It wasn't what I expected and my heart dropped to the floor.
This sort of news isn't supposed to happen so, so soon.
But I'll keep my arms spread wide, and I'll always be around.
You're the love of my life, my wife
We'll get over this overriding tide.
We won't be able to do all the plans that we made,
But I promise your presence will never fade.

—KOURTNY WEDEKING

TUTU ORIGINS

Sometimes great ideas start in unexpected ways. For Linda and her husband, Bob, an intimate gesture between them became a life calling.

Linda and Bob had moved from Arizona to New York but had not had time to fully establish themselves before Linda was diagnosed with breast cancer. Bob, a photographer, was still doing a lot of his professional work in Arizona, which meant that he couldn't always be in New York for Linda's oncology appointments. In an attempt to cheer her up and show his support, he began taking pictures of himself in different locations dressed in a pink tutu. Linda shared the photos with other women as they met for chemotherapy sessions and found that they were therapeutic for others as well. The women looked forward to Bob's new tutu antics as an opportunity to laugh together and ease the long infusion sessions. The photos created solidarity among the women and support for Linda, who was new in New York, far away from friends and family. Linda talked about how that experience sparked a project:

> You are in there, when you are getting the IV chemo, so what are you going to talk about? So I showed the images, and people really liked them. It was interesting because some people just thought it was funny because he was in a tutu, and some people said he really touched their emotions through it. I thought it was pretty cool, and I came one day and told Bob this and said, "Wouldn't it be great if you could do a book of these images and donate it to cancer centers across the US?"

It was a great idea, but only an idea at that point. It needed a lot of development and a lot of work to turn into a reality. As with most successful projects, Bob and Linda needed creativity, skills, money, and a good bit of luck to turn it into something much bigger.

They had a little bit of an advantage: they had worked together for some twenty years on various projects and knew how to get started. They first tried the traditional route with an agent, who didn't work out too well. Then they tried self-publishing but found it too expensive to sustain. A call from a friend pushed them toward the next step of their journey:

> They said, "You have this body of work. What are you going to do with it?" It was just great to have that phone call because I think we were getting very tired. Not burned out—we just didn't know what avenue to take. That pushed us into figuring out what else we could do.

OH, THE PLACES WE HAVE GONE

The next step involved the internet. They launched a website. Linda sent out a letter to about 1,300 people that included Bob's and her mission statement and a request for people to help by buying a print of one of Bob's pictures.

Their story was featured in an article on Yahoo Shine that went viral. They had so much activity on their website that it crashed. The next thing they knew, they had an invitation to appear on the *Today Show*. Linda remarked:

> They did a video on us, and in May of that year [one of their anchors] interviewed us, and we got seven and a half minutes on the *Today Show*, which is phenomenal. That was so much fun. Sure, I was nervous—I was on national television—but

we were really fine-tuning the story. It was a good adventure. How many times am I going to be on the *Today Show?* It was a great experience.

When I got home from the *Today Show,* one of the first calls that I took was from the senior vice president at Bloomingdale's. She said, "I saw your story on the *Today Show.* I loved it. I want to see if there is something we can do together." That started the conversation.

After their TV appearance, Linda and Bob sold so many prints that they were able to start producing the book. Using the proceeds from the book, in turn, they established the Carey Foundation.[30] At first, they struggled with how to make it all work. Starting and running a foundation was a whole new experience:

Where was this money going to go? I don't want to pay for anybody's drugs, just for incidental costs, because cancer is really expensive. We thought we would do more of a grassroots, little thing and give money to people who need help. We had no idea what we were doing. We were flying by the seat of our pants. Every day was a new day of learning. Somebody would come in with something. "How will we resolve this?" "We'll do it this way." It was just crazy.

Linda and Bob ended up with two different entities. The Tutu Project is a campaign based on Bob's photography that raises money to support the work of the Carey Foundation. Bloomingdale's, a major supporter of the Carey Foundation, helped it grow by inviting Bob and Linda to book-signing events at stores all over the country.

---

30 The Carey Foundation's mission is to provide financial support for people diagnosed with breast cancer, survivors, and their family members.

Linda's involvement with the Tutu Project and the Carey Foundation has been life changing for her. They have given her purpose. She has been honored and overwhelmed by the attention of the world and the gratitude of the patients who have been helped by her story or by the funds provided by the Carey Foundation.

Since their humble start, Linda and Bob have been invited all over the world. Their fame and their work continue to grow. Meanwhile, Linda is still fighting cancer and continuing with treatment. She remarked that if you saw her in full makeup on the *Today Show* you would think she was fine and that cancer was no big deal, but it is. She reports that she still has problems with "chemo brain" that make it hard for her to stay focused.

For Linda, what is really important is getting the story out. The tutu part is the fun part. The cancer is the bummer. It is all a balancing act. She is balancing her new work, which is exciting and inspiring, with cancer treatment and all that comes with it. She said:

> I hope that in some way I can inspire other women just to know that there is life with and after cancer. Now I have a little platform available to me, so I really try to develop my end of the story. The whole thing is, I don't want anyone, particularly with metastatic [cancer], to think that it's easy. If I'm being interviewed on television or I'm interviewed wherever, I probably look really good; well, I also have professional makeup, though. I try to figure out some kind of balance so that people know that there's hope, but there are also times when—it's not "Woe is me," but I don't want people to feel bad just because they're having a bad day. It's kind of a tricky balance. So while I'm doing well, I have chemo brain right now.

Chapter 16

TAKING ON THE MISSION: JOSH'S STORY

The author and friend Carol Ann, with LympheDIVAs sleeve.

From "**A Sparrow's Tenor**"

You were a fair-faced dame
The game now changed, so pure
Fragile and withering, just waiting for Aceso's cure.
A long time trapped in the windy storm
But always warm
Always shining bright since birth.
Never stopped fighting
Until the Harpies took you from this Earth.

—KOURTNY WEDEKING

BROTHERLY LOVE

Losing a loved one is hard. We don't all grieve in the same way, and the stages of grief can be scrambled—each stage will come when it comes and will take as long as it takes. People often try to make sense out of tragedy. They try to find a purpose. They don't want their loved one to have died in vain, and finding a purpose related to the cause of death can be helpful. Tom Golden wrote that, especially for men, action is part of healing grief. Men tend to be problem solvers. While women are likely to talk out their pain, men tend to heal through action.[31]

Josh did not have breast cancer, but his sister did. Rachel was just a couple of months shy of her thirty-fifth birthday when she found a lump in her breast. She was diagnosed with stage 3 triple-negative breast cancer. Triple negative is a type of breast cancer that lacks three essential hormone receptors; without these receptors, many traditional breast cancer treatments will not work. Rachel's treatment was aggressive, including chemotherapy, radiation, and surgery. She had a total of nineteen lymph nodes removed during the diagnosis stage. A few months after surgery she began to notice lymphedema, a condition that occurs when lymph nodes are removed and are no longer able to filter fluid from the body. Without the lymph nodes, fluid can back up and cause swelling. The swelling often becomes chronic and leads to other symptoms. The increased size and weight of the arm can cause fatigue and impair daily activities. While these symptoms are bothersome and embarrassing, they can be only the beginning of problems. More severe cases of lymphedema can result in fever, chills, generalized weakness, and recurrent infections and skin

---

31 Thomas R. Golden, *Swallowed by a Snake: The Gift of the Masculine Side of Healing* (Golden Healing Publishing, 1996).

problems in the affected limb. Patients undergoing radiation and chemotherapy are already more susceptible to infections, and lymphedema further increases the likelihood of infection and poor health. While elevating the involved limb and gentle exercise can be helpful, the mainstay of treatment is compression.

Back in 2006, when Rachel was diagnosed, there were very few options for compression garments. Lymphedema was a major problem for her, and she hated the heavy, tight, ugly surgical sleeves that she had to wear to control the swelling. She hated the feel, and she hated the attention they generated. She hated having to explain to everyone that she had breast cancer and what lymphedema was.

LYMPHEDIVAS

Rachel was an athlete. She wanted something that was as comfortable as an athletic compression garment but would do the job of the medical garment. She decided to design something that would fit her needs.

The first sleeves were in bright colors that were more of a fashion statement than an advertisement of cancer. Instead of asking her about her cancer, people asked her where she got her cool sleeve. A company was born. Josh explained:

> One of the big complaints Rachel had was people coming up to her when she was wearing the regular beige one and saying, "Oh my God! What happened to your arm?" And it became a story of breast cancer and lymphedema and all of those negative feelings. Once the LympheDIVAs became the thing, and she was wearing those, it was an approach of "Oh my God! That's so cool! Where'd you get it?" It wasn't about her condition. It wasn't about anything but a fashionable accessory. That creates an easier way to respond about it

and makes it a little bit more positive. When you are dealing with something in a positive manner, your body tends to respond better.

When Rachel died, her company was still "in the red," with more expenditures than income. Her father, a retired physician, took over. Josh wanted to be involved, but his dad advised him to wait until the company was profitable before quitting his paying job. Once that happened, Josh added his skills to the company. LympheDIVAs sleeves eventually added patterns to the bright colors, expanding options for people suffering from lymphedema. While the sleeves are still noticeable, the comments they provoke are often much more about the fashion statement and the attractiveness of the sleeve and much less expressions of pity for the wearer. Josh explained:

> We have over a hundred patterns now. We can put crystals on some of the sleeves so that it gives them a little bit of bling. We are trying to make it easier to deal with for the men and women who have to deal with this and giving them some control over their own conditions. This is something that, once they've got it, they've got it for life if they are managing their edema every day, if they are trying to prevent it. They might just wear it when they are flying or they exercise, but it will still give them some self-confidence and some control about what is going on and be able to make it something that's part of them and also, hopefully, something that isn't as negative.

Josh now finds purpose in the work Rachel started. While he misses his sister, he is honored that he gets to talk about her to people every day. Besides providing a fashionable and comfortable option for lymphedema treatment, he provides education on lymphedema.

He was with Rachel throughout her treatment and felt that discussion of potential side effects of treatment, including lymphedema, was lacking. He is proud of the fact that LympheDIVAs is a company that provides not only a useful product but also public service through education. He talks to breast cancer patients and survivors every day about preventing complications of lymphedema and encourages both patients and their providers to talk more openly about potential side effects of treatment, especially lymphedema.

Josh has continued Rachel's work and helped to make her dream a reality. In doing so, he has found a way to manage his own grief and a new purpose for his life. Both survivors and loved ones need healing beyond the physical. He finds healing in easing the journey for others and in teaching both patients and providers about lymphedema.

Chapter 17

SEEING NANCY IN OTHERS:
BARBARA'S STORY

Barbara the businesswoman.

Falling Leaves

*As new buds emerge hope returns. Spring brings new life,
but a different life. Life before fall is no more. Grieve for
the life lost. Embrace the new. Gather the strength and the
grace of the journey. You will need it for the moments
that you feel alone in your newness. You will need it
to grow into the person you will become.*

—DONNA DeGRACIA

NANCY'S STORY

Barbara's two sisters, Patsy and Kathy, had breast cancer, as did their mother. Whenever possible, Barbara supported her sisters with her presence. On one of her trips to chemotherapy with her sister, Patsy, at a county hospital, Barbara met a young mother named Nancy who was attending her own chemotherapy session with her three young children. Barbara was shocked. She had no idea that people as young Nancy got breast cancer. She explained:

> But the real eye opener was that there were three young children at Nancy's feet because she had no money to pay for childcare and no family that could take off from work to watch her kids. If she was going to get treatment, those babies had to come with her. They were probably five, four, and three or two. The youngest one was still in diapers. And here she was for eight hours with her bag of stuff to try to entertain these kids, and she was getting chemo. I remember thinking, "Oh my gosh! Oh my gosh!"

By the end of the day, Barbara had fallen in love with the children and offered to take Nancy and her kids to their care while her sister, Patsy, waited.

> I finally got Nancy all packed up, and she said, "Barbara, you *can't* do it." I said, "What do you mean I can't do it, Nancy?" She said, "Barbara, I don't have a car. We're taking the bus. We have two changes on the bus. We're going to be fine. It's just the way we get around."

I was appalled. I felt prickles all the way down. Where was my mind? Nancy couldn't afford childcare—how in the world could she afford a car? It was another one of those eye openers for me. Needless to say, we packed Nancy up and the kids and Patsy in Patsy's car, no kid seats or anything, and got everybody where they needed to go.

Barbara's encounter came back to haunt her after Patsy's death. She couldn't stop thinking about Nancy. She was missing her sisters and her mother and wondering why she had been spared when they had not. She had a prophylactic mastectomy and later found out that she was the only one in her family who did not carry the gene. After her sisters died, she was on an emotional roller coaster. She asked "Why?" a lot. She felt a lot of responsibility because she had been spared. Eventually it became important to her to "make a difference" because she was the one who was still alive. Her first responsibility was to family. "Patsy and Kathy did pass away," she said. "I met the commitments I made to my sisters to get all the kids through high school."

Family and work kept Barbara busy, but she felt the need to do more. Her family was spread out, living in three different states, making it complicated to keep her promise.

At the age fifty-four I sat back and thought, "Barbara, you've had a fantastically successful life in the business world. If you want to do something about breast cancer, you better get on it, because you're fifty-four, and you better get going on it. The time is right."

THE HOPE CHEST FOR BREAST CANCER

In the process of her own soul searching, Barbara remembered Nancy and how she and her children had had to change buses several times each way to and from the treatment center for each chemotherapy session. This young woman had made a profound impression on Barbara, who was inspired by the idea of an organization that would help other women struggling with both finances and cancer. She had to be careful and thoughtful, yet daring. In 2001, she left her corporate job and founded Hope Chest for Breast Cancer, an organization aimed at providing for the most urgent needs of breast cancer pateints in treatment. Being a businesswoman, Barbara knew she needed to find a sustainable way to support her foundation:

> So I created the Hope Chest for Breast Cancer retail stores. We sell very upscale furniture, decorative accessories, and designer women's clothing to raise the funds to support the programs I was going to develop. So we had this ongoing revenue stream from our retail stores. We started making money. Our first store opened in the very end of 2002; 2003 was the first full year for our first store in Wayzata [Minnesota]. Our second store opened in 2006 in Saint Paul. Our third store opened in 2013 in Bloomington. The lag between 2006 and 2013 was the recession—I just couldn't invest in another store. Things were just too unknown in the business world. These stores provide the ongoing revenue stream to the foundation.

Barbara didn't want to reinvent the wheel, and she didn't want to make the same mistakes that other nonprofits make. She wanted the money she raised to do the most good possible in the most ways possible. She took her time and did her homework. She developed partnerships and collaborated with other organizations rather than building everything from scratch. Hope Chest developed relationships with local hospitals and clinics and created the Hope Chest Emergency Assistance program. She explained how it works:

> Let me paint you a picture. If you can, envision a young woman getting her treatment for breast cancer, and she just starts sobbing and sobbing. The nurse comes over. "Are you nauseous? Are you blistering? Are you in pain? Let me give you drugs. Let me stop that medication, that drip. I can give you medication. I can make it easier for you." The woman just keeps sobbing. She says, "No, that's not it. That's not it at all. They're turning my electrical services off today. I've got this eighty-six-dollar bill, and I cannot pay it. Social Services called me this morning. They're taking my kids if my utilities get turned off. I have nowhere to turn. I just don't know what to do. I can't go on without my kids." The nurse right there can say, "Give me your electric bill. The Hope Chest will pay it tomorrow."

> The reason we can do that is because we collaborated with the hospitals. We put the Hope Chest Emergency Assistance funds right at the hospital. It is like cash in a drawer. It is that hospital's responsibility to get that bill and get it to their department to write that check and to give a call to that electric company saying, "We're paying off this bill. Don't harass her. It's in the mail." We're taking care of it right then on the spot. The young woman didn't have to do anything. The nurse filled out a one-page form so that we can track who

is getting our information and our money, but that's
it. Her electric bill is paid, and she didn't have to move.
She can stay in her home. She can keep her kids at home.
She can keep the lights on in the home. She can keep the
heat on in the home.

Despite doing her homework, Barbara had a lot to learn.
Experience was her best teacher—she used her own experience
and the experience of those she partnered with to make
improvements in her model and to add much-needed services.
Within a few years, Hope Chest was doing great work, but
it was not enough. After about three years of working with
different hospitals, Barbara brought together a group of medical
professionals and other partners for a "best practices" meeting.
At the end of the meeting, she asked what else was needed.
They said:

> "Barbara, they're not eating well. We're poisoning them.
> Chemo is poison killing everything in their bodies, and they
> need good food in their bodies, good nutrition. They need to
> be strong so they can fight the cancer and let the poison we
> are putting in there do its work." So I said, "That's an easy
> fix. Let's get some grocery-store gift cards—Cub, Rainbow,
> whoever—and we can take care of that."

> They said, "Barb, you're not listening to us. Yes, if we give
> them gift cards they can buy food and put it on the table.
> That's a good thing. But on a longer-term basis they need to
> eat nutritious meals. And if you have bellies to fill and you've
> got money, just enough money to go to the grocery store and
> live, you're going to go down the aisle, down the middle, and

buy processed foods that will fill those tummies up. That's
your number-one concern: to take care of that hungry tummy,
not get nutrition into them."

Another thing they told me, and it's very true for me, is that it's
hard to shop healthy. If you don't know what you're doing, it's
really hard to shop healthy. So I said, "Okay, we'll deliver meals."
So we created the Hope Chest Meals that Heal program.

Initially, Hope Chest partnered with an organization that has
been feeding homebound patients for twenty-five years. They
hired a nutritionist and created meals specifically for the breast
cancer patient. They paid attention to the side effects of chemo
and created mild menus that didn't have any odors or heavy spices.
Their meals were frozen in case patients didn't feel like eating right
after chemo.

 Barbara and her organization had come a long way in realizing
her dream to make a difference. She was happy with the work she
was doing and feeling successful, but she knew the importance of
continual assessment and adaptation.

I thought this was the greatest thing since sliced bread. I was
so proud of the Meals that Heal program. So once again, I
like to meet with the people that we help, so I met with the
volunteers that deliver the meals with the organization we
partner with. They had been doing it for about six months,
and I said, "How's it going? Are they loving it? Is this just the
greatest?" They said, "Barbara, let us paint you a picture." As
you know, pictures don't get painted when things are going
well. So I said, "Okay, paint me the picture."

They said, "Here's a mom. She's got this awesome, delicious chicken-and-rice casserole, a little frozen thing. It looks so good. It's exactly what she needs. It's healthy. It smells delicious. It makes your stomach growl to just see it. And sitting across from Mama are two young kids eating cheap dry cereal because there's no milk in the house. So what does Mama do? Across the table goes that delicious chicken-and-rice dish for her kids."

So we now know the age of every child in the home, and we deliver age-appropriate food for the children. If there is a caretaker in the home, we also will deliver food for them through the Meals that Heal breast cancer program, and we do this the entire time she is in treatment. That's what the Hope Chest does.

The other side of Barbara's work is the fundraising side. The retail stores are a big part of her financial success, but they don't tell the whole story. Several times a year the Hope Chest for Breast Cancer hosts fun-filled events—such as the Fillies Race for Hope racetrack fundraiser—that honor survivors while raising money to help those who are struggling. Barbara herself continues to struggle with her own emotional journey. The Hope Chest is part of her healing.

The emotional part of the rest of the journey kind of came in spurts. I was really down for the first few years after [my mother and sisters] died. I struggled with the whole loss thing, and the why, and with watching their kids struggling, that whole family thing . . . Then I started the Hope Chest. I've been on a real high with the Hope Chest. The emotion piece with the Hope Chest is knowing that we are making a difference, knowing that we've provided over a million dollars to help women and men and the families stay in their home and have that home livable.

One of the things that has come in some of the notes, and sometimes when I've been able to meet the patients, is, "You know, Barbara, our kids were struggling so much. They were so scared. I was a single mom, and I was so, so sick, and my kids were just scared to death, but with your help we not only kept them in their home but we kept them in their school so they didn't have to change schools. They weren't out on the streets. It gave them stability at a time that was so very, very frightening for them." So what happened to Mama was that Mama was a survivor. So that piece is a real high for me.

Chapter 18

FINDING
BALANCE

The author with her certificate of radiation completion.

From "**Hills**"

I'm learning to trust the cycles now
There will always be hills.
Wholeness embraces both dark and light.
I need only concentrate on the present hill
And not worry about hills ahead.

—GAY WALKER

FINDING STRIDE

For Barbara, Josh, and many others, cancer is life altering. It causes pain and suffering, but it can open doors and create purpose. Finding purpose can be an important component of healing.

Balance is an important part of health beliefs in many indigenous cultures, including Native American, Hawaiian, and Chinese. When something bad happens, we need some good to restore balance. Finding a purpose, a way to give back, helps us restore balance after cancer uproots everything. Cancer changes our lives, and it changes the lives of those around us.

Recovery and transformation are not instantaneous. They take time. First, we must heal the body and the spirit and be mindful of changes. Just as the Buddhist practitioner savors the journey of the tea through the body, we must pay attention to the changes. We must be forgiving of our weaknesses, for they are areas for growth. They will become the source of our strength and our learning.

My second cancer diagnosis intruded into all aspects of my life for much longer than I anticipated. Even months after finishing radiation therapy, I was still fighting my way through exhaustion on a daily basis. I had been hoping to get this book to the publisher and was working on other projects that were important to me. Everything was pushed back. I had to back out of some activities that were important to me. I tried to keep pushing, but the more I pushed, the more fatigued I was, and I finally realized my efforts were counterproductive. It was amazing how much joy came from watching a younger colleague flourish when given new and welcome responsibilities and how much my energy level improved when I handed responsibilities over to her.

The balance has been in the learning. I have, of course, learned more about breast cancer and treatment options, but I have also learned more about myself and about the importance of patience. David G. Allen said, "Patience is the calm acceptance that things can happen in a different order than the one you had in mind." That is a lesson worth learning. It is one that echoes the Christian teaching of my childhood, that God has a purpose that we do not understand and that patience is a virtue. I have learned to be more patient with myself.

After the physical healing, we need time to process change. Any change is uncomfortable; it seems ill fitting at first. Later it becomes our new norm. Processing change is very similar to processing grief. It comes in stages that vary from person to person.

It is only after we have healed and processed the changes that we are able to recognize and accept that the sand coming through the narrow part of the hourglass is the same, but different. That is the oxymoron of transformation.

I am not the same little girl who listened to *Peter and the Wolf* with my friends at age four. She is still a part of me, just as those friends who are no longer on this earth are a part of me, but now there is so much more. I think of an image I have seen of a woman who had her chest tattooed by Candice Tekus after mastectomy, turning her scars into a garment of flowers and music, turning pain into beauty. I think, also, of all of the people I have met along the way, people I would not have met except for cancer, and how each one has enriched my life in a different way. Pain and suffering are balanced by beauty and tranquility. Acceptance becomes growth.

Cancer interrupts life. It makes us pause and take stock. It forces us to learn and to grow. Through it all, like the marathoner, we persist, we gain strength, we gain perspective, and we transform lives.

Appendix A

POETRY

Collapse of My Belief System:
A Nativity Scene
BY GAY WALKER

Cancer has made me purge every niche of my belief system.
Expectations are being discarded from the corners of my soul.
Nothing is left untouched or unexamined.
Beliefs never questioned are being cut to the bare bone.
Is there anything left that I can trust?
The contents of my mind are wrung through a wringer
Squeezing out certainties I have held dear.
The entire foundation is crumbling, brick by brick.
All that is left is doubt and fear.
The cupboard is bare and I am so hungry.
How can a lifetime of carefully selected beliefs
evaporate so quickly?

Must I erase the slate clean in order to be reborn,
To come into the world naked?
I am in the birth canal.
Painful contractions press me toward the opening.
Is this what the baby feels in the final stages of labor?
Or the caterpillar emerging from the darkness
of the cocoon?

I long to unfold my wet wings and model their brilliant colors
To see the light and feel the energy of the sun.
I want to fly unburdened
Like a helium balloon unleashed from the weight that held it down.
I yearn to truly know God and be filled with her love.

Cancer

BY AMINA BHATTI

You touch the bodies of the living
And mark them for dead
A plague of their own flesh
Rampant, raging, you spread.
Cruel monster, slithering
Through vessels, unknown
Multiplying, dividing
You plunder, you grow
You ravage and destroy
Rot the body like wood
No care for the innocent
No mercy for the good.
Blood, swelling, horror
When at last you are found
we fight for the victim
to which you are bound
we poison you, poison
hack, gauge you out
burn you, hot waves
just kill you somehow
internal struggles, a war
that won't make the news
sometimes we win
and sometimes
we lose.

The Fact Is

BY MORRY EDWARDS

The fact is we don't know
yet
No fractionated equation
with precisely weighted factors
tells us how the DNA
unravels
spinning cells out of order
chaotically trampling
their neighbors

What part Red Dye #3, sugar highs, omega-6 fats?
What part spiritual commitment or disconnection?
Alignment of stars?
Trapped in your job or an unfulfilling relationship?
Lost dreams?
Exposed to radon?
Too many dental x-rays, mammograms, or
mercury fillings?

Or just a minimal added daily dose of radiation?
Not washing your fruit enough?
Fertilizing your golf course too much?
Pesticides mimicking estrogen?
Having too little sex or too much sex?
Parrot feathers in the vent?
Cellular phones, power lines, or stray microwaves?
A blackened heart?
Not dancing enough?
Barbecuing too much?

So we believe with our biases
or we deny with our biases
and live our lives
until we are visited
to sort through the
mystery and find
our path

Is It a Dichotomy or an Oxymoron That Turns into a Paradox?

BY MORRY EDWARDS

Like jumbo shrimp
People roll their red-stalked eyes
in disbelief,
not synthesizing the incongruous
when a cancer patient states,
"It was the best thing that ever happened to me."
"It was a gift."
"I was dying until I got the cancer."

Mortality aside, it was "bittersweet" at the least,
if you can't quite make the above claims.
What else can be said when death blows its
sweet/sour breath in your face
Filling your lungs with desire
to breathe in one molecule of oxygen at a time
and set each moment on fire.

People want you to "act naturally,"
like you ran over a speed bump
instead of a cliff.

Hegel understood dichotomies
like fear and freedom
scared to death
free to live
synthesis from
the mutually exclusive
to an uncomfortable juxtaposition
changing from a dichotomy
to an oxymoron and settling into a paradox
as you
live with cancer.

2 a.m.

BY GAY WALKER

A cast of characters visits me at 2 a.m.
They conveniently hide during the day,
making their grand entrance only in the darkness.

After the diagnosis
Mr. Fear wakes me up at 2 a.m.
What is happening to me?
Am I going to die?

After the lumpectomy
Mr. Indecision wakes me at 2 a.m.
Should I do things I abhor and fear
Radiation and chemo to save the breast
Or cut it off and be done with it?

After the mastectomy
Mr. Pain wakes me at 2 a.m.
Every little move reminds me of his presence.

After the healing has begun
Mr. Indecision returns at 2 a.m.
Should I do reconstruction? Tram flap or implant?
How can I choose between two imperfect solutions?
Fear returns periodically reminding me . . .
People die of this you know.
What if it comes back?

After the tissue expander surgery
Mr. Pain's army appears at 2 a.m., spitting fire and stabbing me.

Vicodin—the sword keeps them at bay
After four hours they start creeping back.
Mr. Fear makes another entrance
Did I do the right thing?

After each of ten weekly expansions
Mr. Pain's army returns at 2 a.m.
standing guard in four-hour shifts
After three nights they disappear
Until next week's reserves come

After tamoxifen
Mr. Hot Flash sneaks up at 2 a.m., again at 5 a.m.
With no warning he turns up the thermostat
Broiling, dripping wet.
Mr. Indecision asks if I can keep this up for five years.

After three uterine polyp removals (they keep growing back)
Mr. Fear wakes me at 2 a.m.
Is cancer now growing in my uterus caused by tamoxifen?
Should I have the uterus removed and continue tamoxifen?
Should I stop tamoxifen and hope breast cancer does not return?
Answers are nowhere in sight.

My wish—to be like a baby who sleeps through the night
I want my daytime cast of characters
Ms. Hope, Ms. Inner Strength, and Ms. Positive
to be with me all the time.

Healing Shelter

BY JULIETTA CHEVALIER

Welcome to our humble home,
a shelter from the rain.
And temporary refuge
from unnecessary pain.
Where broken hearts and
battered wings
and anger, fear and shame
can find some quiet comfort . . .
you don't have to explain.

After time has healed your hearts
and mended broken wings,
inventory honestly life's most important things.
Questions only you can know
the answers to so well
can set you free forever
from your own private hell.

You are stronger than you know
for you've survived this war.
And still inside have courage
to stand and take no more.
No longer are you victim,
for now you have control.
So take what you have learned here
and liberate your soul!

The True Miracle

BY MORRY EDWARDS

Inside the Miracle
eye of the storm
a stillness
flashing true understanding
of purpose not cause

We never resolve the mystery of
Cancer's intrusion nor
what helped cure the physical disease

but the true Miracle
is not cure
but what is healed
the spark ignited
that fires future with promise

Hills

BY GAY WALKER

After the purchase of a new Schwinn bike
I am aware of hills.
I never noticed how many there are
until cycling uphill.
Little ones hardly noticed
surprise my new bike legs.
Each hill an effort to climb.
Huffing and puffing
I become the little train that could.

Triumphantly I reach the top
Legs relax—a time to coast
No pedaling necessary
Like a bird soaring on the wind
An interlude of ease.

But then, another hill
another challenge.
There is a rhythm to this.
After each hill—another appears.
Each hill has two faces
Stress and relax
Tension and freedom
Pushing and allowing.
Yin/yang
The rhythm of life.

Breast cancer has been my steepest hill.
I have crested it and found healing on the other side.
Rhythms and cycles
Challenges and healing.

Always another hill to climb
just as I thought I was finished.
Diagnosis, treatment, reconstruction, five surgeries
Now a sleeper hill appears.
Endometrial polyps—potential cancer on the horizon.
I didn't expect this hill
Anticipating, I change gears
It is steeper than I thought!
Shift into low gear
Pedal faster with less tension
I must reach the top
before coasting to freedom.

I'm learning to trust the cycles now
There will always be hills.
Wholeness embraces both dark and light.
I need only concentrate on the present hill
And not worry about hills ahead.

Prayer for the Ministering Women

BY MARY LANDRY DECKER

*Our dear friend Mary, a woman of small stature and large heart,
has come home to her cabin in the pine trees to begin a process of
transformation. The doctors say they can do nothing. It appears
that her body is growing too small and frail to tether such a great
rambunctious spirit to this earth much longer.*

*And so the midwife women come, as they have since time began,
expressing with imperfect hearts and hands a perfect divine love.*

*Comes the nurse woman, gifting with bottles of many-colored pills,
anointing with a gentle touch.*

*From far away comes the childhood friend,
bringing memories no one else can share.*

*Comes the organizer with calendars and lists in one hand
and a phone in the other. She gives of her time.*

*One comes enveloped in soapy steam and the scent of bleach and
lemons. With strong hands, she smooths freshly laundered linens
on Mary's bed. She dispenses laughter.*

*The kitchen magician comes. With her wooden spoon, she can
transform humble ingredients into the most exotic, succulent dishes!*

*The quiltmaker brings her pieces of colored cloth, tosses them into the
air, and catches them in the most beautiful arrangement.*

Another can grab pictures out of the thin air and show us to ourselves.

Gardener woman plunges her hands into the dark secret earth and brings out flowers of brightness and beauty.

One comes bearing a fragrant loaf of freshly baked bread. She has kneaded her life force into it with her passion.

The one who wears "purple from the neck up" shepherds us. When she passes, you can faintly hear the sound of drums, harps, and cymbals. Her robes are scented with the smoke from ancient sacred fires.

The grieving woman comes. She offers her living broken heart. She shows us how to turn sorrow into grace.

The night watcher comes to wait in the night. She eases the pain and guards against the fears that haunt the darkness.

Mother Father God, you have given us our talents, and we offer them back to you as gifts.

Our medicines, steaming towels, bubble baths, chicken stock, jokes, flowers, music, and our full hearts.

Medicine woman God, we ask that your healing power flow through our hands to Mary.

Let our touch be your touch.
Infuse her medicines with your grace.

Healer of our memories, you see into our hearts.
Please mend the hurtful parts of our past.
Remove the scars that block the flow of your healing energy.

Author of time, your time is not our time. You have placed infinity in
every second, a universe in every cell. Give Mary all the time
she needs to finish her earthly tasks. You who orders the planets
in space, order Mary's cells to you will.

And in Mary's small cottage, let her find all the space
she needs so that she can feel your cool soothing breath around
her. For the midwives do not control the birth, but gently allow the
passage of power. It is between mother and child, from the
mother, through the mother, to the mother.

Washer woman God, shine us up!

Joker woman God, we see your face in the sacrament of laughter.
Your joy is on the other side of sorrow.

Nurturing God, we praise you in the kitchen!
We thank you for good-smelling food and sweet life.

Needlewoman God, sew our many colors together.
Harmonize us and we will cover Mary
with a quilt of your comfort and peace.

Picture-making God, shine your light into our dark places.
Give us clear vision.

Master gardener, we are your flowers.
Weed out what is not good in our bodies and spirits.

Mother God, first nurturer, cradle us. You created us from love,
and in your constant love you hold us.

Bakerwoman God, knead our cramps, our aching muscles, our
rigidities of body and spirit. Smooth us! Braid us together. Bake of us
a beautiful loaf! Then we can feed each other with ourselves.

Grieving God, mend all our brokenness. Give us your peace.

Guardian of the night, let us feel your presence in the night when
we are afraid. Shine your light on Mary's path, if she goes where we
cannot follow. Hold her hand in the dark, so she never feels alone.
Calm her fears with your Motherlove, for she is our sister but your
true child. You give us the night so we can see the beauty of the stars.

For all that we ask,
For all that we are given,
We thank you.

Here I Sit

BY SUSAN PETTIT

Here I sit in my chemo chair—reminiscing about my hair.

As I look around at all the faces,
I realize cancer comes from many places.

It does not discriminate based on short or tall
and
doesn't care if you are big or small.

We sit in our chairs minding our own business as the IV drips . . .
drips continuous.

Sometimes the room is full to the brim
and other times it seems I am the only one in.

As I continue to sit and receive my treatment
I look around with pure amazement.

People are talking and chatting with friends,
you would never know we are all sick and just hoping to mend.

There is a sense of connection where words are unspoken.
We are all fighting a piece inside that has shattered and broken.

Cancer thinks it can take our courage and spirit
but if you ask anyone here they will say "no way—I won't let it."

So as the drip drip of the IV comes to an end,
I am grateful for these strangers who
I know deep down are really all God's friends

How Do You Feel?

BY GAY WALKER

May 20, 1998
Bed 919, oncology surgery floor
totally out of context for me.
Rush Presbyterian St. Luke's Hospital
I welcome the big gun pain pills
and struggle to find a position
that hurts the least
Sleep tries to elude me
I'm trying to find peace
in my suddenly chaotic life

At 5:30 a.m., May 21
A knock on the door
it bursts open
Lights abruptly glare overhead
A peppy resident doctor appears.

How do you feel? She chirps

Is she kidding?
Sleep had let me escape
from pain and cancer
And she brought it back
with a flip of a switch.
Damn it. Can't this wait?

How do I feel?
I feel like an elephant
stepped on my chest.
I feel like I was hit
by a Mack truck.
I've been wounded

Do you have to wake me to remind me?

How do I feel?
I just became a statistic
a research subject.
Can't you support my healing process
let me adjust to this intrusion in my life?
Please put your duty aside
till the sun wakes up.

How do I feel?
I don't know how I feel about MY cancer!
Part of my femininity has been cut off.
Dissected and trashed like garbage.
I've been wounded.

How do I feel?
I've been cheated.
This wasn't supposed to happen to me.
I've been a good girl,
a poster child for healthy living.
No illness was supposed to attack me.

I've gotten to know cancer (from arm's length)
As the therapist who
guides OTHER people with this illness.
I expected immunity
in exchange for my work
It was a bargain with life
I thought I had made.

How do I feel?
Maybe it's all a mistake
Not meant for me.
Someone will discover it
and take it away.

We Remember Them

BY BESS KUZMA

ADAPTED FROM A POEM BY RABBI SYLVAN KAMENS AND RABBI JACK RIEMER

As our alarm greets us before dawn making a call to rise;
We remember them.
As we don our scrubs in the dim light of the morning
so as not to wake our loved ones;
We remember them.
As we sip our coffee and prepare to face what the new day brings;
We remember them.
As we drive through traffic away from the comforts
of home and family;
We remember them.

As the noise and bustle of the hospital fills our ears;
We remember them.
As we walk by colleagues already busy at work on the floor;
We remember them.
As long as we practice, we will sacrifice for those we care for as,
We remember them.

When our hearts are struck with grief as we
deliver unwelcome news;
We remember them.
When we feel we can no longer move forward past our tears;
We remember them.
When we are forced to make decisions for those who cannot speak;
We remember them.
When we see the smiles in the eyes of those we have helped;
We remember them.
When we return home and try to quiet our busy minds;
We remember them.
For as long as we can work, their memories will live with us,
for they are now a part of us as,
We remember them.

Electric Lady

BY JULIETTA CHEVALIER

Electric Lady, you know it's you
and what it is that you must do
with what lies buried deep inside of you.
So please, Electric Lady, don't be blue.

You shine so bright from inner light.
It's darkness that you fear.
Stop anger and hate; let Love radiate
with each unfolding year.

It's time to change—you know it's true.
Bring out the child who's locked in you.
Though it can hurt to feel so much,
the world needs your perceptive touch.

Don't blame yourself or feel confused.
What's done is done; we all stand accused.
No limits now, except for doubt.
So scribble your true colors out.

Electric Lady, I need you now.
Electric Lady, find me . . . somehow.
Electric Lady, please shine on me.
Electric Lady, don't cease to be!

A Sparrow's Tenor

BY KOURTNY WEDEKING

It's been a long time since I was your young naïve lamb
Too young to understand.
Although I was intuitive of your imminent asphyctic changes
So strange and something that cannot be rearranged.
I felt your stone cold wrist
You were pretty as a picture in a silk case topped with roses
As the ground closes in.
Now I'm getting older, Dad says I'd make you proud.
Just know, I've never been without
Because you've been the angel on my shoulder.

You were a fair-faced dame
The game now changed, so pure
Fragile and withering, just waiting for Aceso's cure.
A long time trapped in the windy storm
But always warm
Always shining bright since birth.
Never stopped fighting
Until the Harpies took you from this Earth.

It was an April Sunday
I loved seeing you walk through that door.
It wasn't what I expected and my heart dropped to the floor.
This sort of news isn't supposed to happen so, so soon.
But I'll keep my arms spread wide, and I'll always be around.
You're the love of my life, my wife
We'll get over this overriding tide.
We won't be able to do all the plans that we made,
But I promise your presence will never fade.
The children that we made, I'll keep safe
But please be my guide as they get older
And be the angel on my shoulder.

You were a fair-faced dame
The game now changed, so pure
Fragile and withering just waiting for Aceso's cure.
A long time trapped in the windy storm
But always warm
Always shining bright since birth.
Never stopped fighting
Until the Harpies took you from this Earth.

I've never been here before
So offshore from the life I envisioned.
Married to a good man with two young kids, amid
A showering storm with winds so strong
That keep knocking, blocking me from my El Dorado.
But I'm strong, I will prove my body wrong
I will fight through every single night
Until the anesthesia takes over.

This isn't easy, it's the hardest thing I've done
As I go beneath the blade, so afraid
And the chemicals run through my blood
If this fails, I'll sail because I love the life I've run
And I'll be your beholder as the angel on your shoulder.

I was a fair-faced dame
The game now changed, so pure
Fragile and withering just waiting for Aceso's cure.
I spent a long time trapped in the windy storm
Always warm
Always shining bright since birth.
I'll never stop fighting
Until the Harpies take me from this Earth.

Obituary:
Right Breast of Gay Walker.
Age 54. Richland, MI

BY GAY WALKER

*Passed away May 20, 1998 at
Rush Presbyterian St. Luke's
Hospital, Chicago after a short
battle with cancer. Right Breast
was born February 1, 1944 to
Gay Walker. She was an active
member of Gay's femininity
team. She was loved by John
Walker during their thirty-two years of
marriage. She nursed Gay's two
children, Kristian, age 27, and
Heather, age 24. She is survived
by her twin sister, Left Breast.
She was proceeded in death by
the right breast of Gay's mother,
Dorothy Startzman, and aunt,
Doris Egemeier, twins, age 84.
Interment at University
Pathology Department.
Private
memorial services have been
held.
Memorial contributions
may be made to the Right
Breast Reconstruction Fund.*

Falling Leaves

BY DONNA DeGRACIA

*It is fall. The trees are brilliant against the clear blue sky.
I remind myself that this beauty is part of the process of death and
rebirth. Fall is the reprieve before the harshness of winter.
But even that cold, bleak season has moments
of breathtaking beauty.*

*The colors of the fall leaves would be less brilliant without the
glow of the sun. Likewise, the journey of the patient would be less
bearable without the love and support of family and friends. It is in
the individual's darkest hour that she relies on the strength of those
around her. In putting aside pride and accepting support she discovers
her own strength is intertwined with many. Fear subsides,
replaced for a moment by peace and gratitude.
She can rest for a moment in the
warmth of love.*

*As fall progresses the leaves will fall to the ground, leaving the trees
naked and exposed with gnarled branches reaching desperately for
the sky, reminiscent of the breast cancer patient ravaged by treatment
and marked with scars. Like the trees, she is suspended in waiting,
waiting for the treatment to end and the healing to begin,
waiting for the pain to end and
eternal peace to begin.*

The winter can be harsh. Gray clouds laden with
storms obscure the warmth of the sun. Cold winds scatter
hopes and rattle faith. Broken relationships flee like dry leaves
across the crusted snow, leaving only the
frigid fingers of death.

As new buds emerge, hope returns.
Spring brings new life, but a different life.
Life before fall is no more. Grieve for the life lost.
Embrace the new. Gather the strength and the grace of the journey.
You will need it for the moments that you feel alone in your newness.
You will need it to grow into the person
you will become.

Baring My Soul

BY GAY WALKER
JUNE 1998

I'm hiding behind my Reach to Recovery bra
A handful of fluff to match my orphan
makes me look normal.
No one can see the wound.

Mary, spokesperson for a group of friends, asks
"Will you show us your scar?"
For a moment, I don't want to be exposed.
And yet, this is something I must face
Who better than with friends!

There is tension for all in this request
Most have never seen a mastectomy scar
having only imagined horrible disfigurement
And I, wanting to be normal,
not treated like a freak or sick person,
decide to be courageous
dare to bare and share.

I unhook my bra with the fiberfill
and after a brief pause and a deep breath
I expose the battlefield on my chest.
A tight red dart runs where fullness was.
Once hidden ribs ripple the surface.
Reminiscent of a little girl.

"It's so neat and healed looking"—they agree.
No huge black stitches.
"Not so bad," someone says.

The task is to accept who I am,
to find wholeness despite distortion.
Being open with my friends is important,
I can cover up for strangers.
Someday I will be open with strangers.

Cancer

BY BETH LABRECHE

pills, bills
tears, fears
relief, disbelief
mad, sad
care, swear
hope, dope
time . . . more time . . . no time
pink, stink
hell, well
scars, stars
worse, curse
soul, hole
barf, scarf
hair . . . more hair . . . no hair
prick, sick
cry, sigh
life, knife
die, deny

plead, concede

incision, decision

talk, balk

vex, sex

grow, woe

speak, seek

worry, hurry

thief, grief

god . . . more god . . . no god

hug, slug

operation, separation

rad, glad

family . . . more family . . . no family

pray, play

make, break

cancer . . . more cancer . . . no cancer

cancer, no answer

cancer, your answer

Appendix B

OTHER CONTRIBUTIONS

What to Expect during Surgery

BY LAURA BLESSE

In most places, you are brought to a holding area prior to surgery. This is where you are kept immediately before being taken back to the operating room, and it is where the surgical team makes sure everything is prepared for your operation. The amount of time spent here is variable depending on the facility as well as how the surgical schedule is running. Some facilities allow family members into this area while others will not. You may want to bring a book or activity to keep you occupied while you are waiting.

You will be seen by quite a few members of the surgical team. If you do not already have an IV in place, you will have one put in at this time. You may notice that you are being asked the same questions by different people. This is normal and is actually part of the surgical protocol to make sure that you are having the correct surgery and understand the surgery you are about to have. You will be seen by the anesthesia team. If you have had any issues with anesthesia with past surgeries, please be sure to mention it to them. Just prior to being taken back, you may be given a dose of medication to help you relax. If you are given this medication, your memory may be a little fuzzy. Some people are able to remember things after they are given this medication, whereas others are not.

When everything is ready, you will be wheeled back into the operating room (OR). You may see the surgical tables with instruments on them. You may hear some noises as the team continues setting things up. Everything that you see and hear is to get your procedure running as quickly and smoothly as possible. There are usually about five to six people in the room—one or two anesthesia team members, a surgical technician (assists and hands instruments to the surgeon or assistant), a circulating nurse, an assistant (often a physician assistant), and your surgeon. Depending on the exact surgery you are having done, there may be even more team members.

You will move from your bed onto the OR table. The rooms are kept cool to keep the amount of germs to a minimum. As soon as possible, the staff will grab you warm blankets, but they may not be able to do so until you are safely on the OR table. Once you are lying down, your arms will be placed on boards to the sides. A strap will be placed across your abdomen or legs, and your arms will also be secured to make sure they do not fall down once you are asleep. A number of monitoring devices will be placed on you—a pulse oximeter on your finger to measure the oxygen concentration in your blood, electrocardiogram (EKG) leads on your chest or back to monitor your heart, and a cuff on your arm to measure your blood pressure.

The anesthesia team will place an oxygen mask over your face and ask you to take deep breaths. When they are ready, they will let you know that they are starting to administer the anesthesia. Depending on what medication they are using, it may burn a little when it goes into the IV. You will be asleep within a few seconds. You will not have any awareness during the surgery.

The anesthesia team typically wakes you up while you are still in the operating room. However, because of the medications you were given, you may not remember this. Most people do not remember anything until they have reached the recovery area. You will be moved back onto your bed and wheeled into the recovery area. In the recovery area you are closely monitored for a period of one to two hours. The nurses will check your vital signs regularly and make sure you are not having any pain or nausea.

Your doctor will update your family in the waiting area. As long as you have not had any complications, you will be able to leave the recovery area within two hours. From this point you will either be discharged home or admitted to the hospital, depending on what surgery you had done.

ABOUT SURGICAL CHOICES

Surgery is the treatment of choice for the majority of breast cancers. It is easy to be overwhelmed with your treatment options, and it is important that you understand them before making any decisions. If you are confused with anything your physicians have told you, please do not hesitate to ask them to clarify. This is an important choice to make, and you should be certain that it is the right one for you.

Fortunately, breast surgery is typically not very risky. It is not done emergently, which means that if you have any other health issues (such as heart or lung conditions), these can be brought under control before having surgery, making it safer for you. This also means that you may get a little more time to consider your options. Sometimes the type of disease or other factors, such as your health status, dictate what treatment would be best. This section will discuss the surgical options for patients requiring mastectomy. Usually it is up to the patient whether they wish to have reconstruction and when they would like this reconstruction performed. I will not discuss the specific forms of reconstructive surgery.

In general, there are three major options for those requiring mastectomy:

1) Mastectomy alone without reconstructive surgery:
This option is for patients who wish to have their breast removed and not have additional surgery. Where the breast previously was

will appear as a flat area of skin. Some people choose this because they have had a previous mastectomy on the other side or are having a double mastectomy and do not wish to have their breasts present. Some do not want to have implants in. Some may opt to use external prosthetics that are placed in the bra. Some may not want prosthetics at all.

2) Mastectomy with immediate reconstruction: This option is for patients who would like to have their mastectomy and reconstructive surgery done as one procedure. This means that they will only undergo anesthesia once and will only recover from surgery once. Because more is being done to the patient, it is a longer procedure and may result in a longer hospitalization. Due to the increased length of surgical time and potential hospitalization, patients may be at a higher risk for infection.[1] Some studies report that women who have immediate reconstructive surgery may fare better psychologically, as their bodies appear similar to how they did prior to surgery.[2] However, even with reconstruction, these patients are still dealing with the loss of the breast as it previously was, and this is upsetting and stressful.

3) Mastectomy with delayed reconstruction: This option is for patients who would like to have their mastectomy and then have a reconstructive surgery as a separate procedure at a later date. Since the individual surgeries are smaller, patients may require little or no hospitalization after their procedures. Patients will have to undergo anesthesia two separate times. This surgery is typically done after the patient has completed any other necessary breast cancer treatment, and the patient may even be considered to be in remission. Because of this, the patient may be under less stress than they would have been earlier and may be better equipped to make decisions.

Ultimately, the options listed above are very similar in their surgical risk factors. Unless there are other complicating factors, such as preoperative or postoperative treatment (including chemotherapy or radiation) or other health factors at play, the patient's voice should be the deciding factor. If you opt for reconstruction, you should discuss the specific type with your doctor. What is best or possible for you will depend on several things, such as the nature of your cancer, the need for postoperative treatment with radiation and chemotherapy, and whether you have any conditions that might prevent tissue being taken from another area in your body. Once you have made the decision to have a reconstructive procedure, you can discuss your options with your surgeon.

REFERENCES:

1. National Nosocomial Infections Surveillance System. "National Nosocomial Infections Surveillance (NIIS) System Report, Data Summary From January 1992 Through June 2004," American Journal of Infection Control 32, no. 8 (October 2004): 470–485.

2. Zhong T, McCarthy C, Min S, Zhang J, Beber B, Pusic A, Hofer S.. "Patient Satisfaction and Health-Related Quality of Life After Autologous Tissue Breast Reconstruction: A Prospective Analysis of Early Postoperative Outcomes," Cancer 118, no. 6 (March 2012): 1701–1709.

This Is How I Will Remember You

A SHORT STORY BY EMILY ARNASON CASEY
IN MEMORY OF KRIS ARNASON DILLEY, 1960–2014

My aunt was diagnosed with inflammatory breast cancer in the spring of
2008. She lived six difficult but beautiful years with cancer. She was and
remains a survivor in the hearts and minds of all who love her.

This is how I will remember you: sitting at the bonfire on an August
night, the stars in the sky like sparks thrown from your hands,
scattered. Your face tanned and narrow and eyes lit with flame.

There you are on the deck at the cabin with a book spread
open in your lap, and Grandma is coming out the door, coffee in
hand. You are standing behind the sauna splitting wood; you are
sitting in your corner spot in the sauna, sweating buckets, yelling,
"Throw another blast on, Trish." You are diving off the end of the
dock and swimming underwater as far as your lungs will let you,
and when you surface you're halfway to the Point. You roll on
your back and breathe, floating, before your young, beautiful body
swims you to shore. You were always half fish; we all were.

This is how I will remember you: laughing, holding your sister,
singing in your twin off-note voices, "Sisters, sisters, we were
always such devoted sisters . . ." while Grandma shakes her head
and lights another cigarette and us girls—all piled onto the couch
together—squeal with laughter.

This is how I will remember you: driving that damn red car
you told me you loved because "it was all paid off," my first and
perhaps only lesson on money. There are five or six or seven of
us girls crammed into the back seat, and you and your sister, my
mother, are singing something again, and Grandma is telling you
to shut up, and we are laughing. Our heads are tied with scarves,
and our knobby knees are smashed together—a dozen bruises and
scratches between us. And you'll berry-pick until Karissa and I lie
down in the grass and claim we're dead, until Grandma storms off

to the car, until the little ones fall asleep in the grass. Later, in the cool of a rainy afternoon, you'll make jar after jar of jam, enough to keep you through the winter; you know come February you'll need a little taste of summer on your morning toast.

This is how I will remember you: your grandbabies on your lap, in your arms, at your side. Your hands busy sewing quilts and blankets and bags and dresses because your art was given in love. And I will remember the poet auntie who wrote of raising her children, of her own childhood, of her Icelandic heritage, of her marriage. I will remember the student who loved Shakespeare classes and wanted to be an English teacher.

I will remember the crazy lady that you were: a woman perhaps who never quite fit into the confines of her time. A woman who wanted to travel with her daughters, to write poetry, to read great books, and to sew. A woman who loved shopping for her grandkids, decorating her apartment, watching TV dramas. A woman who most of all wanted to be with her family at the lake every summer.

★

You never wanted to be defined by your disease and thus refused to attend support groups. You said you would fight cancer, and you did. You never stopped fighting. But cancer is a disease inside a human body, and the body is not a battlefield. Death is not defeat. I wasn't there in the end. I didn't see you go; I wasn't at your side as you slipped out. I hadn't seen you in months. And when I saw you again you looked like Grandma, laid there, so quiet now. I was grateful for everything you'd given me and for the lessons you had taught me that I had not yet realized. I was grateful for your love and your life. I was grateful too for all your blatant flaws, your humanness so evident at times, and for all the annoying things you did and said because all that pushed me to realize what it actually means to love a person, another human being. So flawed, so lonely and lost—so filled with grace. We will suffer in this life. But we need not suffer alone.

★

I will remember the books you put into your hands and read year after year until they changed you and the day you promised me five dollars if I read *A Tree Grows in Brooklyn*, and when I did I understood you a little better. I will remember the years when you ate sunflower seeds all day, spitting out the shells onto a paper plate at the cabin, and the peanuts you ate only after breaking them in two and removing the little Santa Claus head from the middle. I will remember the pies and the cakes and the cookies you made because, as your daughter would say, sometimes we need to feed the soul.

How proud you were of me for studying English and for writing. How proud you were of yourself when you studied and wrote and planned a different future. There were the times you drove me crazy, the times I wanted to scream at you. But then you were there in front of me laughing and telling your stories and making jokes and calling us "honey," and I couldn't stay mad for long.

I will remember your hands and your feet and the slope of your shoulders as you walked down the road, away, always lost in your own world. I will remember the way you daydreamed and loved and believed in us all—your three daughters, your nieces and nephews. I will remember your courage in facing death and your refusal to give up your life. I will remember your passion. I will remember the way you believed there was good in us all.

This is how I will remember you: with your blond hair and your tanned skin in the heart of summer, sitting in peace, quiet and alone, listening and watching and knowing the things you knew, the secrets like tiny poems that shattered in your lap, in your hands, from your lips and disappeared. Fleeting, as always, the world. Beauty like shadow at dusk on an August night when the echo of voices rings the loudest and the children are still splashing in the lake, unwilling to come in for the night, to give up the water and find their beds and their honeyed dreams. And you, always you, will be there in that twinkling light—the best light of day—the hour when the day is nearly done and our hearts are full, our minds ready, when dreams come easy.

Appendix C

SELF BREAST EXAM
TECHNIQUE

Technique for the breast self-examination is important. When I taught students to do a clinical breast exam, I taught them to do it in three positions: 1) sitting leaning forward with the breast hanging away from the chest wall; 2) sitting up straight with hands pressed together or pressed against the hips to tense the chest muscles in order to observe any dimpling; and 3) lying back or with support under the side being examined. The first position allows for gentle palpation (feeling) for lumps on the surface of the breast, including the underside. The second position allows for visual inspection of the breasts to make sure they move symmetrically and that there are no areas that are fixed to the chest wall. The third position is for deep palpation to appreciate any lumps that may not be on the surface.

The area to be examined is larger than most people would expect. It extends from the clavicle (collar bone) to several inches below the breasts and from the center of the sternum (breastbone) to the middle of the axilla (armpit). It is important to look at the breasts. Look for changes in the skin, including changes in coloration or texture. One particular type of breast cancer can make the skin look like an orange peel.

It is important to look closely at the nipples and the areolas or rings around the nipples. Are both nipples pointing outward? If not, have they always looked the way they do now? Some people have one or both nipples inverted; this is only a problem if it is a change. Pinch the nipples gently. Nothing should come out of the nipples unless you are breastfeeding. Breast discharge does not necessarily mean cancer, but it should be evaluated.

Finally, it is important to feel for lumps at different levels. Go up and down the chest wall in straight lines, like how you would mow a lawn, making sure not to miss any areas. Move your fingers in small circles, examining three different levels: surface, midlevel, and deep toward the chest wall. For home breast exams I recommend checking the breasts in front of a mirror and in the shower, where the warm water and soap make it easier to appreciate differences in breast tissue.

Doing a good breast exam takes practice. If it is not done correctly it is easy to miss an abnormal finding, so be careful of the false reassurance that a "normal" breast self-exam means that everything is fine. I would recommend that anyone wanting to do self-exams consult with a medical provider and learn how to do a careful and complete exam. Instructions can also be found online—the National Breast Cancer Foundation, breastcancer.org, and Susan G. Komen all provide information on breast self-exams.

Appendix D

CONTRIBUTORS

MEGAN AYERS ASSAD

Megan Ayers Assad is a physician assistant who graduated from the St. Catherine University master's of physician assistant studies program in Saint Paul, Minnesota. Megan is a wife and proud mother of two growing boys.

AMINA BHATTI

Amina Bhatti describes herself as a part-time poet and newly qualified doctor based in Nottinghamshire, England. In the online world, her poetry alter ego is Heartful Whispers, but in the real world, she is just an average British Pakistani girl sitting in a cafe, trying to look artsy.

LAURA BLESSE

Laura Blesse is a physician assistant from Cleveland, Ohio. She works in surgery at the Cleveland Clinic. Laura is the author of articles on breast surgery and related topics that have been published in peer-reviewed journals.

ANITA BUEL

Back in 1983 there were no interpreter requirements at medical appointments.

Going through surgery and treatments was a frustrating experience with little access to communication. Deaf community is an important part of Anita Buel's life and led her to form the Deaf support group called Pink Deafies. This support group wanted to do more for community. Director Barbara Allen, coproducers Nancy Meyers and Anita, and a community of friends created a ninety-minute documentary film of Deaf women telling their breast cancer journeys called *Signing On*. The film has won many awards and recognition throughout the country.

It was discovered in 2008 that she has a BRCA1 mutation. Anita has two daughters and enjoys her time with five grandchildren. Each day is a blessing.

EMILY CASEY

Emily Arnason Casey is a writer, teacher, and mother living in Burlington, Vermont, with her two young sons and husband. The oldest of six children—five of whom are women—she grew up in northern Minnesota. Her maternal grandma was diagnosed with breast cancer twice and survived into old age; her aunt died of inflammatory breast cancer in 2014. Her writing has appeared in literary journals and an anthology of Vermont writers.

SARAH CAWLEY

Sarah Cawley was diagnosed at age thirty-two with stage 2 invasive ductal carcinoma, ER/PR+, and HER2−, and underwent a mastectomy, chemo, radiation, and then a prophylactic mastectomy, choosing not to have reconstruction.

When she's not fighting cancer, she's working as a physician assistant, distance running, and caring for her husband and two daughters.

JULIETTA CHEVALIER

Julietta Chevalier is a yoga instructor and hypnotherapist as well as the owner of a hammock yoga studio in Flint, Michigan. She also writes poetry, teaches art, and has a hand-engraving business that specializes in small and unusually shaped items and heirlooms. More of Julietta's poetry can be found at juliettasplace.com.

LISSETH DEGRACIA

Lisseth DeGracia is a nurse and a mother of three. Lisseth began her nursing career in oncology, where she used her family experience with cancer to provide care and understanding to her patients and their families. Besides work and family, Lisseth enjoys bodybuilding and weight lifting.

MORRY EDWARDS

Morry Edwards, PhD, is a licensed psychologist and senior fellow of the Biofeedback Certification International Alliance who has specialized in treating people with head injuries, cancer, and other chronic illnesses for almost forty years. He is an advocate of the holistic approach to health and wellness and encourages patients to take an active role in their treatment. Formerly director of psychological services at the West Michigan Cancer Center, he is currently located at Neuropsychology Associates in Kalamazoo, Michigan, and consults in several clinical settings. He is also a part-time instructor at Kalamazoo Valley Community College. Morry has made numerous national presentations and published many articles and self-help manuals, including *Almost Instant Holistic Stress Management for Almost Anyone, Hope for Headache Relief, Some of the Best and Worst Things to Say or Do for Anyone with Cancer, Hope for Pain Relief, Brain Boosters, 10 Key Principles to Maintain Motivation,* and *MindBody Cancer Wellness: A Self-Help Stress Management Manual.*

DIANE ERICKSON

Diane Erickson was a forty-seven-year-old at-home mom to three teens when she was diagnosed with stage 3a triple-positive, node-positive invasive ductal carcinoma. She placed her trust in God and her medical team and has journeyed through bilateral mastectomies (no reconstruction), chemo, Herceptin, radiation, lymphedema, and continuing aromatase inhibitor therapy while reaping the benefits of acupuncture, massage, green smoothies, walking, napping, and the love and prayers of her husband, family, and friends. Thriving beyond cancer for nine years and counting, Diane is committed to comforting others with the same comfort she has received from Christ (2 Corinthians 1:3–5) as a Firefly Sisterhood guide and as cofounder and coordinator of the Comfort Club, a Christian breast cancer support group in the Twin Cities (comfort.club@gmail.com).

BARBARA HENSLEY

Losing her mother and both of her sisters to breast cancer devastated Barbara Hensley. During their combined six-year battle, she became painfully aware of the challenges faced by underserved women. Seeing women already struggling just to afford rent and food, then being faced with fighting breast cancer disturbed and angered her. So she did something! In 2001, Barbara resigned her corporate executive position and founded the Hope Chest for Breast Cancer, where she chairs the foundation and is CEO of both Hope Chest Franchising and LeeRyan Corporation.

Barbara has a bachelor of arts degree from Austin College, a master's degree in business information management from the University of Missouri, and a master's degree in urban affairs from Webster University. She is a current member of the Minnesota Women's Economic Roundtable and the TwinWest, Saint Paul, and Wayzata Chambers of Commerce as well as a past member of the board of directors of the Breast Cancer Awareness Association.

DICK HURRELBRINK

Dick Hurrelbrink and Maren Hed met at the University of Colorado and were married for twenty-three years before Maren's death from breast cancer in 2010. Dick continues to live and work in the Twin Cities and spends as much time as he can with their sons, Tucker and Duncan.

HALIMA KASUNGU

Halima Kasungu works with a nonprofit called Tanzania Women Cancer Care Support and Advocacy Foundation (TWOCCAFO). It is made up of breast and cervical cancer survivors and offers outreach, counseling, support, and advocacy. The organization's Reach for Recovery program is very useful for those undergoing surgery, treatment, or recovery. Staff do hospital visits, home care, and provision of prostheses and bras; they also have a women's church group called Shepherd of Good Hope, whose members have volunteered to offer shelter and food to those rural women without food or means of survival when they come for treatment in the only cancer center in Dar es Salaam. There is no other facility in the country apart from Ocean Road Cancer Institute and the private Aga Khan Hospital in Dar es Salaam. They are working under difficult conditions and are looking for partners for support and networking opportunities.

BESS KUZMA

Bess Kuzma is a physician assistant working in northern Minnesota. Her adaptation of "We Remember Them" was created as a humanities assignment during her clinical rotations. It represents her respect for those who have died and reflects her Jewish faith.

BETH LABRECHE

Beth LaBreche was born in Tokyo, Japan, after her parents, who were missionaries, were evacuated from Korea due to the Korean War. The family returned to South Korea after the war. Beth grew up in Daejeon, South Korea, and graduated from Korea Christian

Academy in 1968 before attending Baldwin Wallace University, graduating cum laude in 1972 with a bachelor's in music education. Beth left teaching when she moved to Minnesota and married her husband, John LaBreche. She worked for the University of Minnesota for thirty years before retiring to become a full-time grandmother. Beth and John have lived in the same house in Fridley, Minnesota, for thirty-eight years. In 2003 Beth was diagnosed with lobular cancer in situ and had a mastectomy. She enjoys a number of hobbies and thrift-store shopping.

LINDA LANCASTER-CAREY

Linda Lancaster-Carey, the president of the Carey Foundation, was first diagnosed with breast cancer in 2003. She and her husband, Bob, have used photography both for personal healing and to raise money for their nonprofit, which supports women through their breast cancer journey.

MARY LANDRY DECKER

Mary Landry Decker is a photographer in South Haven, Michigan, who has written poetry about the breast cancer journey.

JOSH LEVIN

Josh Levin became president of LympheDIVAs (www.lymphedivas.com) in 2010, three years after his sister passed away from breast cancer. Before joining LympheDIVAs, Josh had several different career lives. After graduating from Brandeis University with a major in psychology and minors in philosophy and classics, he started his professional life in public relations and website management for Blissworld (including Bliss Day Spas, Bliss products, and the BlissOut catalog) but moved into digital project management for the advertising firm FCBi after two years.

After gaining this experience, he returned to graduate school for a completely unrelated field: underwater archaeology. He graduated from Texas A&M University with a master's in anthropology and returned to New York City to work for the consulting firm Frog Design as a project manager. After ascending the corporate ladder to associate director, he joined LympheDIVAs, where he is able to bridge his product, project management, and public relations experience to continue his sister's mission to help those suffering from lymphedema both physically and emotionally.

CHRISTIAN LOGER

Christian Loger proudly serves as mammography service manager of the Jane Brattain Breast Center (www.healthpartners.com/care/specialty-centers/jane-brattain-breast-center/). An alumnus of Luther College and Concordia Graduate School of Business, he brings extensive experience in medical administration to the Park-Nicollet system. His management style blends a passion for excellence with a caring compassion in his relationships with patients and staff.

KRIS NEWCOMER

Executive director Kris Newcomer believes the Firefly Sisterhood is her "Barbara" project. Two of the closest people in her life, both named Barbara, are breast cancer survivors, and when she was asked to build the organization, it was a chance to give back in a way that melded career experience and skills with a passion to make a difference.

The Firefly Sisterhood focuses on living the mission of fostering one-to-one connections, with over sixty volunteers and one staff person dedicated to the one-to-one program. In the first year alone, the organization helped seventy-five women dealing with a breast cancer diagnosis. But for Kris, there are many more Barbaras out there to offer hope, create a connection, and light the way home. www.fireflysisterhood.org

ANNIE PASCHALL-ZIMBEL

Annie Zimbel is a professional psychic, tarot card reader, comedian, and actress who lives in Saint Paul, Minnesota. As a new empty nester, she is out and about in the world laughing, playing, and creating opportunities for herself and others to change the way they look at things or each other.

Through laughter she moves forward, becoming ever so much more unstoppable and leading people in that same direction for themselves.

Through her readings and comedy, she "helps you help yourself." To find Annie, check out her website at www.AnnieZimbel-A2Z.com. If you need some laughter or someone to talk to, give Annie a call, and she will work to make you feel and be better.

CAROL ANN PETERSEN

Carol Ann Peterson is the manager of patient support and education at Frauenshuh Cancer Center (https://www.healthpartners.com/care/find/doctors/frauenshuh-cancer-center/). She is honored to work on behalf of patients and families as they make their way living with cancer. Her background in palliative care, hospice, community health, education, holistic health, and spiritual direction brings a breadth, depth, and sensitivity to her work that has proven to be a valuable and helpful resource to patients, family members, and caregivers. Areas of ongoing interest include loss, grief, transition, resiliency, transformation, and capacity building. She looks forward to supporting you on your journey.

TARA RICK

Tara Rick is a physician assistant in oncology and urgent care as well as a board member for the Foundation for Cancer Care in Tanzania (www.tanzaniacancercare.org). Tara has a particular interest in breast cancer and women's health globally.

KELLY ROSAR

Kelly Rosar is a married mom of two. She lives in Ham Lake, Minnesota, and works as a medical assistant in urgent care.

LISA ROSENTHAL

Lisa Rosenthal spent her career in the judicial system prior to her diagnosis with metastatic breast cancer. She lived in Minnesota for a number of years but returned to her home state of Maryland to be near family as her cancer advanced. She passed away on May 18, 2015.

CAROLYN AND ROGER TEACHWORTH

Carolyn Teachworth was diagnosed with breast cancer when she was fifty-four. She was born in South Dakota and was raised in South Dakota and Montana, so she has a lot of Western practicality. She started golfing when she was eleven, and it has been her one constant passion in life. She shot an 88 the first time out after two years of treatment and recovery. (Very proud of that). Her three male playing partners of twenty-five years, including her husband, Roger, took her with them in a cart when she was not strong enough to play. Roger and Carolyn have been married twenty-five years, and she has two stepchildren and two grandchildren. Carolyn received her undergraduate and graduate degrees in South Dakota and taught accounting at Loras College in Iowa before coming to her present position as the corporate comptroller for the company where she has worked for twenty-nine years.

MOLLY THEISEN

Molly Theisen is an active mom who enjoys fitness, traveling, adventures with her family, reading, and spending quality time with her sweet pug, Otis!

GAY WALKER

Gay Walker is the program coordinator of integrative holistic health and wellness in the College of Health and Human Services at Western Michigan University in Kalamazoo, Michigan (www.wmich.edu/holistic). Her background is in art therapy. Her own journey with breast cancer gave her life a new direction as an art therapist, helping others through their own journeys and helping students in a variety of health fields learn to do the same.

KOURTNY WEDEKING

Kourtny Wedeking is a graduate of the St. Catherine University master's in physician assistant studies program and works in geriatric medicine. Kourtny lost her mother to cancer at a young age.

Other contributors chose to remain anonymous.

Appendix E

WEBSITES OF INTEREST

This list is by no means complete. It is a list of websites that I have come across during my research or that friends have shared with me.

SCREENING GUIDELINES AND RESOURCES

American Cancer Society Guidelines for the Early Detection of Cancer: www.cancer.org/healthy/find-cancer-early/cancer-screening-guidelines/american-cancer-society-guidelines-for-the-early-detection-of-cancer.html

American College of Obstetricians and Gynecologists (ACOG) Guidelines: www.acog.org/About-ACOG/News-Room/News-Releases/2017/ACOG-Revises-Breast-Cancer-Screening-Guidance--ObGyns-Promote-Shared-Decision-Making

Center for Disease Control and Prevention Comparison of Various Guidelines: www.cdc.gov/cancer/breast/pdf/BreastCancerScreeningGuidelines.pdf

National Breast and Cervical Cancer Early Detection Program: https://www.cdc.gov/cancer/nbccedp/about.htm

US Preventive Services Task Force Guidelines: https://www.uspreventiveservicestaskforce.org/uspstf/recommendation/breast-cancer-screening

BREAST CANCER EDUCATION

Bright Pink: www.brightpink.org

Cancer Treatment Centers of America: www.cancercenter.com/breast-cancer

Know Your Lemons: www.knowyourlemons.com

Komen Educational Materials: ww5.komen.org/BreastCancer/KomenEducationalMaterials.html

Komen Tools and Resources: ww5.komen.org/AboutBreastCancer/ToolsandResources/ToolsResources.html

RESOURCES FOR SURVIVORS AND CAREGIVERS

Breast Cancer Education Association: www.breastcancereducation.org

Breastcancer.org: www.breastcancer.org

Cancer Legal Care: www.cancerlegalcare.org

Caring Bridge: www.caringbridge.org

Care Calendar: www.carecalendar.org

The Carey Foundation: www.careyfoundation.org

Cleaning for a Reason: www.cleaningforareason.org

Komen Tools and Resources: ww5.komen.org/AboutBreastCancer/ ToolsandResources/ToolsResources.html

Living Beyond Breast Cancer: www.lbbc.org

Lump to Laughter: www.lumptolaughter.org

LympheDIVAs: www.lymphedivas.com

Men Against Breast Cancer: www.menagainstbreastcancer.org

National Cancer Institute on Complementary and Alternative Medicine: www.cancer.gov/about-cancer/treatment/cam

National Comprehensive Cancer Network: www.nccn.com

National Lymphedema Network: www.lymphnet.org

Oncology Nursing Society: www.ons.org

Sharsheret: www.sharsheret.org

Young Survival Coalition: www.youngsurvival.org

MINNESOTA-SPECIFIC RESOURCES

Angel Foundation: www.mnangel.org

The Firefly Sisterhood: www.fireflysisterhood.org

Gilda's Club Twin Cities: www.gildasclubtwincities.org

The Hope Chest for Breast Cancer: www.hopechest.com

Minnesota Cancer Alliance: www.mncanceralliance.org

Sage: www.health.state.mn.us/diseases/cancer/sage/about/index.html

OTHER WEBSITES OF INTEREST

Foundation for Cancer Care in Tanzania: www.tanzaniacancercare.org

Knitted Knockers: www.knittedknockers.org/make-a-knocker

The Scar Project: www.thescarproject.org

The Tutu Project: www.thetutuproject.com